The **Clifden** Anthology

DISCARD

editor **Brendan Flynn**

...mmunity Arts Week

1995

This book is published by
Clifden Community Arts Week,
Clifden Community School,
Clifden, County Galway, Ireland.

Clifden Community Arts Week receives financial
assistance from The Arts Council/An Chomhairle Ealaíon

Cover Design from a poster for Clifden Community Arts
Week 1992 by Joe Boske.
Typeset by Yellow Banana, Dublin
First published in the Republic of Ireland 1995
Printed by Colour Books Ltd. Baldoyle, County Dublin.

BEV

Contents

for
Brother Killian Kearney

Introduction

The introduction of Transition Year into the Irish Education System was indeed a welcome development. It has meant that the 1994-95 Transition Year class at Clifden Community School could afford the creative time and energy to assemble this anthology of works by writers who have visited Clifden Arts Week since its inception. The students shared an energy and enthusiasm which was always flowing over with a spirit of excitement and adventure—something like the happiness and joy that the writers themselves brought to our school and community since Richard Murphy first read here in 1969.

Exams at times are very stressful. They can make too many demands, at an enormous price to some people. Transition Year has allowed schools to take time which will allow students to sit at the well and think, smell the flowers and create dreams.

A note of sadness has entered the anthology with the sudden death, prior to publication, of Seán Dunne—one of the first to accept the invitation to contribute. I hope that students will be able to take time out and discover places of meditation and rest, something that was so special in Seán's work.

Anthologies are useful books to have. They can be easily packed and taken on a journey. When I was in school I read, besides anthologies, books about poets in order to find new poets and new poems to excite and brighten the imagination. The students over the past seventeen years have got something special from all the contributors—rays of light to brighten up the darkness. Now with the publication of this book the contributors and students may also help to ease the financial pressures which arise yearly in the mounting of Clifden Arts Week.

In his classic book on fairy tales, THE USES OF ENCHANTMENT, Bruno Bettelheim stated: 'Our greatest need and most difficult achievement is to find meaning in our lives'. The visits by the contributors to THE CLIFDEN ANTHOLOGY continue to help all of us to walk the road ahead with confidence.

Our hope is that you will find pleasure among these pages for many years to come.

Brendan Flynn
Clifden Community School
September, 1995.

Tim Robinson

WALKING OUT TO THE ISLANDS

'Interdigitation' is the fine term I overhear the scientists using for the way in which one natural zone meets another along a complex boundary of salients and re-entrants; the close-set come-and-go of its syllables is almost enough to convey the word's meaning, but etymologically it is a little inadequate to such cases as this Connemara coastline where land and sea not only entwine their crooked fingers but each element abandons particles of itself temporarily or permanently to the clutch of the other.

An outline map of this area showing nothing but the boundary between land and water might well be misread unless it indicated which was which. To the bays that ramify into inlets and creeks correspond the peninsulas with their subsidiary headlands and spits; the lakes of the bogland are sometimes linked into archipelago-like sequences, as the major islands are joined by causeways; there are matching ambiguities too, lakes that become inlets at high tide, and islands that can be reached on foot when the tide is out. This last category appealed to me even more than the true islands I had to hire a boatman to reach.

When a few years ago I was mapping the Burren uplands on the south of Galway Bay, and even earlier during a time of walking in Provence that found expression in a series of geometrical abstract works rather than a map, I had become aware of certain experiences of the traveller that do not depend on anything in the nature of the terrain apart from its topography. The most easily conveyed of these is that high point of awareness one reaches in crossing a pass, where the line of the knowable, leading over from the lowland already traversed to that just being revealed, is intersected by the axis of the heights on either side which are left unvisited and unknowable by this journey. The completing of a circuit of an island is another of these purely topographical sensations, the promises and illusions of which I am exploring at length on the

Aran Isles. In Connemara I identified a third, this visiting of quasi-islands by foot.

A little anxiety sharpens the business. Such a visit is an island in time too, a narrow space allotted by the tides; will the slight pressure one is under help to crystallise one's impressions or merely crumple them? Sometimes one has to wait for the parting of the waters as for the curtain-up of a play, which wakes high expectations. Some of these intermittent islands of Connemara are still inhabited, but only by one or two people, and so to visit them is to visit a person, and the topography of 'walking out to islands' becomes an image of personal contact, a metaphor one lives out in concrete reality. I remember vividly two such intertidal episodes, one played out in a suite of green fields beached on wide sands, the other on a rocky pyramid among plunging, folding, silvery rivers of ebb and flow.

I had chosen a day of spring tide for the first of these occasions, and although I suppose this made little difference to my ration of time to be spent on the island, it certainly heightened the stealthy drama of the unsheeting of the sea's bed. I loitered about the deserted strand wondering where was the best point from which to strike out for what was still an island half a mile offshore. The sea-weedy rocks I picked my way along did not link up into a route, the sandy bottomed pools between them were too deep to wade, and nothing seemed to be changing. Then far away on shining levels near the horizon I saw a pair of little figures trudging outwards—women going to gather winkles round the island. I had been aiming off at entirely the wrong angle; I went back along the shore and followed in their steps over freshly rippled sand and fleeting shallows. The island put out a gangplank of damp gold towards me, but as I approached it seemed to retire behind the pale sand-cliffs of its dunes.

I had already heard of old Tomás, the last of his family, who still spent most of his time on the island although he often slept in the houses of various mainland relatives and would probably soon settle down in Ros a' Mhíl. As I crested the dunes I saw him in the distance on a slight rise, looking about his empty fields, and it was immediately clear that this was how he passed most of his island hours. He was the only moving object in my field of vision, and I in his, though his movements as he watched me approach were merely a scarecrow's slight turning and leanings with the wind.

He greeted me courteously when I spoke to him in Irish, and invited me into his house which stood nearby, a little apart from the line of roofless cottages that marked the long axis of the island like the vertebrae of a beached carcass. It was a stone-built cottage of the traditional type, its thatch replaced by roofing-felt, with a loft above each end-room and a central kitchen open to the gaunt roof-space. I sat on the only chair by an empty hearth while he boiled a kettle for tea on a ring set on the nozzle of a gas-cylinder. There was nothing in the room except the frayed and bleached wares of the strandline, of which he showed me from a collection of little things on the windowsill a wave-worn cigarette lighter and a small disc of mica. I would be welcome to stay the night, he told me, but when I explained that I had to return 'by this ebb' he stood up immediately to show me round the island. As we went out he showed me the trophies he still wins every year for dancing jigs at the local festivals.

He moved lightly before me over the low and broken stone walls of the pallid autumnal fields, in which the twisted rootstocks of wild iris showed everywhere among the scant grass. We looked at the unfenced burial-ground with its graves marked only by little boulders and unnamed except in the oral record which would soon leave the island to fade away with this old man, and of which I jotted down a mere scrap: that the grave in the north-west corner is of a woman, said to have been the first settler here, who was drowned when coming into the island on horseback, three hundred years ago. We crossed the grassy street of the skeletal village and took a barely discernible path, once called The Scholars' Road, down to Schoolhouse Beach. Rabbits, flourishing unhunted, had undermined the walls of the deserted schoolhouse and it had totally collapsed. To the south, the ocean-face, a third of the island was smothering in sand as the rabbits tunnelled the dunes and then ate them bare until the winter gales broke them up and set the sand marching. Tomás showed me where the lads used to play football on green fields when he was young; but the fields had fled since then, revealing low foundations of ancient habitations and the heaps of limpet, mussel and winkle shells left by some shore-folk of the island's dateless past.

On the way back to the house we lingered along the strand and examined the offerings of the last high tide. The writing on a plastic bottle we decided was Hungarian. A lavatory-brush puzzled Tomás until I explained its use, which however did not much interest him, and it was for its appearance that he carried it home.

When we reached his house he suddenly dodged inside before me and ran to rap on the bedroom door, shouting 'Get up! Get up! Are you all in bed yet?'—and then turning to me with a laughing face flung open the door to show me the room empty save for a blanket or two on the floor. The only adequate response to his joke would have been to promise to stay with him there for the rest of his life, indeed to have settled down, repelled the sands and repopulated the island. But the tide of my life was set in another direction, and it was already time to walk out of his world.

Paul Durcan

THE HAY-CARRIER

after Veronica Bolay

Have you ever saved hay in Mayo in the rain?
Have you ever made hay in Mayo in the sun?
Have you ever carried above your head a haycock on a
pitchfork?
Have you ever slept in a haybarn on the road from Mayo
into Egypt?
I am a hay-carrier.
My father was a hay-carrier.
My mother was a hay-carrier.
My brothers were hay-carriers.
My sisters were hay-carriers.
My wife is a hay-carrier.
My son is a hay-carrier.
His sons are hay-carriers.
His daughters are hay-carriers.
We were always all hay-carriers.
We will always be hay-carriers.
For the great gate of night stands painted red—
And all of heaven lies waiting to be fed.

Nuala Ní Dhomhnaill

MO MHÁISTIR DORCHA

Táimse in aimsir ag an mbás
eadrainn tá coinníollacha tairrice
réitiomair le chéile ar feadh tréimhse is spás
aimsire, achar roinnt bliana is lae mar a cheapas-sa.

Bhuaileas leis ag margadh na saoire.
D'iarr sé orm an rabhas hire-áilte.
'Is maith mar a tharla; máistir ag lorg cailín
is cailín ag lorg máistir'.

Ní rabhas ach in aois a naoi déag
nuair a chuas leis ar dtúis faoi chonradh.
Do shíneas mo láimh leis an bpár
is bhí sé láithreach ina mhargadh.

Do chuir sé a chrúcaí im lár
cé nar thug sé brútáil ná drochíde orm.
Ba chosúla le greas suirí nó grá
an caidreamh a bhí eadrainn.

Is tugaim a tháinte dubha chun abhann,
buaibh úd na n-adharca fada.
Luíonn siad síos i móinéir.
Bím á n-aoireacht ar chnoic san imigéin
atá glas agus féarach.

Seolaim ar imeall an uisce iad
is gaibheann siad scíth agus suaimhneas.
Treoraím lem shlat is lem bhachall iad
trí ghleannta an uaignis.

Is siúlaim leo suas ar an ard
mar a mbíonn sciollam na móna le blaiseadh acu
is tagann míobhán orm i mbarr an mháma
nuair a chím faid mo radhairc uaim ag leathadh

a thailte is méid a ríochta,
an domhan mór ba dhóigh leat faoina ghlaic aige
is cloisim sa mhodardhoircheacht bróin
na hanamnacha ag éamh is ag sioscadh ann.

Is tá sé féin saibhir thar meon.
Tá trucailí óir agus seoda aige.
Ní bheadh i gcarn airgid Déamair
ach cac capaill suas leo.

Ó táimse in aimsir ag an mbás
is baolach ná beidh mé saor riamh uaidh.
Ní heol dom mo thuarastal ná mo phá
nó an bhfaighidh mé cead aighnis.

Michael Davitt

'TINA G'

Tina:
'Sea, agus mar bhuile scoir anocht
ar 'Chaint na nDaoine'
roinnt foirmeacha aniar.
Let's have a look again at Séamaisín
ag comhrá lena Dhaideo:

> S.   *Foc thú, a chuint.*
> D.   *Foc thú fhéin, a chuint, thú fhéin.*
> S.   *Focáil leat anois a sheanfrigger liath 'dtigh a'*
> *friggin deabhail.*
> D.   *Focáil thú fhéin friggin leat 'dtigh a' friggin*
> *deabhail nó siubhálfaidh mé do friggin*
> *cloigeann suas poll do friggin thóna.*

Tina:
'Sea, feicimid go bhfuil na holdtimers ag
teacht isteach ar an gcaint nua
slowly but surely.
Oíche amárach, an aidiacht bhriathartha
i gcanúint Mhuigh Eo theas (sin focail
ar nós foodpoisoneáiltí) agus éabhlóid
an fhorainn choibhneasta sna hAll Irish Schools.
Until then, Slán. Nó Goodbye, mar a deir
muintir Dhún Chaoin. Nó daoibhse up there
in Gweedore, Cheerio!

Seán Dunne

ONE SUNDAY IN THE GEARAGH
(for Trish Edelstein)

In the long grass of the Gearagh
  You stretch and sleep
   Your head at an angle to my head

A moth flits
 And hovers above you
  Makes a light brooch in your hair

Cows mooch in damp fields
 Lazy heads lifted
  When we pass on thin paths

Stumps of trees around us
 A drowned forest and a drowned
  Village Called Annahala

Lichen on trees, moss on stones,
 Sparrows—nifty commas—
  Dart on the sky's wide page

I tell you of the man who rowed
 Across the waters to his house,
  And drowned on his way home

Afternoon of perfume
 Flowers crushed beneath feet
  Scents yielded like secrets

Bog-cotton in a meadow
 Lighter than your hair
  Your fingers lighter than leaves

Your face smooth against mine
A slim wind between us
The ghost of an old argument

Scanning the lake for otters
We settle for paired swans
White porcelain among reeds

Islands stud the waters
Legions of the drowned
Raising their torn heads

Meadows shimmer with movement
Tortoise-shell and meadow brown
Butterflies in a haze of heat

I stroke your closed eyes
And kiss the lids. I nudge
The tip of each light lash.

Oak stumps everywhere
Suppurating wounds
The black days we have known

A heron stands
Sentry over water
Curled initial on vellum

As we cross old quarry roads
Hands linked like branches
Or rose-trees in a ballad

Jack Harte

HIS FIRST JOB

Michael was three weeks working for the Turf Company when the ganger announced that they were all to go footing turf the following day. It was no surprise, for they had been watching the neat rows of sods drying in the June sunshine; each day, as they crossed the flat expanse of turf spread out on the bank, the men would stoop to lift a sod and note the hardening crust on the exposed surface.

It was curious to Michael that although the men talked about the money they would earn, working at piece-rate on the footing, there seemed to be little joy in their voices. Michael himself was looking forward to the footing, for he was determined to save money that summer. He was on holidays from school and since he was over sixteen he was entitled to get his employment cards and take a job on the bog. The following year he would finish school and, if he got a scholarship, would go to the University. He would need a lot of money.

"Come on, lad, are you getting tired?" Jim O'Donnell called to him and doubled back to help him finish his piece.

They were tidying a clamp of turf that stretched from one end of the bog to the other, a distance of five miles. There were six of them on the job, all seasoned labourers except for Michael, and they had covered about a mile since he had joined them.

The other men were finished their strips and were standing, waiting. They were very helpful and treated him with a fatherly concern, sometimes sending him on an errand when they thought he was growing tired.

"We'll take one more strip each and then we'll go for the dinner," said Christy O'Brien. "It's the last time we'll be paid for sitting down so we may as well make the most of it."

They paced the side of the clamp and took another five yards each. This time Michael did not pause: he gathered up the sods that were scattered at the base and threw them up on top of the clamp. When he had tightened up the base he arranged the sods on the side, sloping them from top to bottom so that the rain would not penetrate into the clamp. It was a job that was usually done in the autumn after the turf was collected, but, as the men explained, the Company had been short of money and could not afford to keep the usual quota of labourers over the previous autumn and winter; as a result jobs like this had been neglected.

This time they finished simultaneously. They had to walk back where they had started in the morning to collect their coats and bags. Before them the clamp on which they had toiled stretched out to the horizon where it converged with the two wide turf banks and the trench between them; even the parallel clamp beyond the far bank seemed to converge with all in a perfect exercise of perspective.

They crossed the turf on the bank and walked down along the trench to where the fire was lit. The fire was in the bottom of the trench because it would be a hazard if lit in any other place. Michael enjoyed dinner-time on the bog; and the men sat around while the billy-cans boiled, and spun yarns. They were all from different parts of the country and each man's yarn was usually based in his own homeland with each man moved by an obligation to top the other man's story. The men from the south were by far the best story-tellers and the only one who could compete was Jim O'Donnell from Donegal. Michael seldom spoke, for as soon as he opened his mouth he became conscious of his youth in the company of adults, and he stuttered and forgot what he was about to say. But he was satisfied to listen.

That day the talk moved from the 'back home' yarns to a discussion on gangers. It was dangerous to get on the wrong side of them, everyone agreed. They were ordinary workers like everyone else until they were given the book and pencil; then they walked on all and sundry to show how much they had come on in the world.

"I'll never forget the way they 'did in' the German," said Christy O'Brien. "They didn't like him from the start. They used to call him 'the Nazi'. When the winter came they gave him a German shovel (they said he ought to be able to use it) and put him digging a drain down in the new bog they were reclaiming to open trench seven. They put him on piece-rate. The poor man! No sooner would he have a few yards dug, than the fresh bog would start closing in again. The gangers would make a point not to call on him to measure the drain until there was no more evidence of a drain than a thin scrape on the surface of the bog. Then they would tell him they couldn't count any drain that wasn't eighteen inches wide at the bottom and that he would have to go back over the whole thing. He had no more than two pounds in wages after the rent for his house was deducted. And there was nothing he could do. He had a wife and family and if he gave up the job they would be thrown out of the house. Well, the German stuck it through the winter, but in February there was a spell of fierce weather to the world, there was sleet and frost. He folded up then. He caught pneumonia. You see his system was run-down for lack of nourishment, and he died."

That story horrified Michael. He knew the German well, a refugee and a very quiet individual. After his death his wife and family left the district and it was rumoured that they had returned to Germany.

A silence fell over the men when Christy had finished his tale. Each man had a story like it but had no desire to talk, instead they each sat brooding. Michael felt uneasy and turned to Jim O'Donnell.

"What is it like, footing?" he asked.
"It's different," replied Jim. "You'll earn more money because you'll be on piece-rate, but you'll work for it."

There was an ominous ring to the words. At that moment Jim didn't seem anxious to discuss it further and gazed down the bog where the great bagger, humbled by distance, was scooping peat from the bank with monotonous regularity and pumping it out through the long spread-arm for a hundred yards; every two minutes there was a flash as the plates of the spread-arm dipped to drop the new line of sods on the bank.

"What are the plots like at the top of the bank?" Christy asked generally.
"They're fairly good," replied a youngish labourer that Michael didn't know. "I passed them the other day and they seemed to be fairly good."
"I think we ought to go up this evening and take a plot each, tomorrow the whole bog will be flooded with men, women and children."

They all nodded their heads to Christy's suggestion. It was agreed. That evening as the half-past-five locomotive chugged up the rails towards the yard, the men jumped one after another from the wagon doorway. They climbed over the clamp of turf and came to the beginning of the bank. The turf was dry and light and each man took a plot, marking it by footing a row of turf along the top. Michael took a plot. This type of footing was new to him as he was used to the traditional method of standing the sods on their ends and propping them against one another, a method always employed with hand-won turf. Now he had to lay two sods on the ground with a little space between them and across them he had to lay two more; thus he continued building until the footing was about two feet high.

When the men had finished their rows they departed and Michael was left alone on the bog. At first the peace and solitude pleased him, however, after a little while he grew lonely, and soon after that the intensity of the silence began to terrify him, for there wasn't a sign of movement in the whole expanse of bog, and not so much as a bird's whistle to suggest the existence of a single living thing. Michael finished his row as quickly as he could and

before leaving made a note of the number that was written on a timber lath at the top of the plot.

The next morning there were hundreds of people on the turf bank. There were men and women, boys and girls. The sight of so many people suggested an atmosphere of festivity and Michael rejoiced in the prospect of companionship. The dark brown of the up-turned sods in the footing contrasted with the light brown of the spread turf, and the dark brown ran in an ever-widening line along the top of the turf-bank.

Michael found it easy to get into the rhythm of footing in the new manner, but being stooped all the time, his back soon began to stiffen. When he straightened up it ached terribly. He made slow but steady progress and was not far behind the rest at dinner-time.

As usual, at one o'clock he gathered up his coat and bag and set off in the direction of the fore. However, there were very few of the men stopping. Jim O'Donnell had his young son in the bog and was sending him to make the tea, while Christy O'Brien and three other men had joined together so that one could fetch the tea while the others continued working. At the fire there were only a few children waiting for cans and kettles to boil and Michael had to eat his dinner alone.

When he was returning to his plot people were sitting down for their meal, but no sooner had he started to work again than they resumed working also. He was well behind everyone now, but he wasn't worried as his father was coming in the evening to help him.

Michael was very tired by six o'clock and was relieved and happy to see the familiar gait of his father coming up along the trench. His father had a billy-can full of hot tea and they both sat down and ate.

When they had finished eating they set to work once more.
"I was looking at the plots as I was coming up the bog," said his father, "and there are some very bad in the hollow. They should be taken up by the time you have this one finished though. If they aren't, try and avoid having to take one. You'd be stuck for a

week in one of those plots."

"Are they near them yet?" enquired Michael.

"Ay, they're within a few plots of the real bad ones."

"I should miss them so. I'm behind everyone, so they will all be up there before me."

They worked for an hour and a half, and made rapid progress. Then his father, finishing a row, said: "I think we'll quit. You have done enough for today. It's heavy work and there's no use killing yourself."

As they left the bog Michael noticed that few people had ceased working yet.

After two days the plot was almost finished and early on the third day Michael was ready for his second plot. He walked down the bank which was now covered with dark brown footings for a distance of half a mile. Most people were finished their plots, and many seemed to be taking a rest lying at the base of the clamp.

When Michael reached the end of the footings he threw down his bag and coat and took the next vacant plot. It was down in a hollow and the turf was wet and soft where water had lodged. In addition, the rows were pitched very closely together so that each sod was stuck to the next and they were difficult to separate. When he put them on a footing they frequently crumbled.

Before he was half-way through his first row many people arrived: the next plot was quickly taken and the next one and the next. Michael was surprised to see Christy O'Brien and others now taking plots, he thought that Christy had finished his one the evening before. A suspicion led him on a walk past the new plots and he saw that the turf in them was dry and well spaced. He returned to his own: it was soggy and ugly-looking. He had been cheated.

Michael felt like crying. He cursed bitterly under his breath at the people in the succeeding plots; he'd show them. He tackled the turf again with determination and speed. But the sods disintegrated in his hands, they were wet and heavy, and by the time he put the fourth pair on a footing the whole structure collapsed.

That evening his father moaned when he saw the plot.

"Didn't I tell you to watch out, that they were bad down here in the hollow. Sure you won't have this done before Christmas. How in the name of Christ did you get this and all the people who were finished before you."

"I think they were holding back and waiting for this one to be taken. They all came as soon as I started."

"Of course they did," said his father, "and they're all laughing at you now, the bastards."

Michael looked into the gulf of disappointment in his father's eyes and he was frightened. He looked away, at the bent figures strung out along the bog; he had hatred in his heart.

His father started to work without a further word; that evening they did a quarter of the amount they had done on the previous evenings. The next day Michael brought his young brother, Tommy, to the bog; Tommy made the tea in the morning and at dinner-time — Michael no longer wanted to go to the fire for his dinner — and did some footing as well.

Towards evening they were visited by the ganger. He came slowly down through the rows of footings, examining them, poking them with a white lath he had in his hand.

"Good God, Young Conway," he bellowed, "this isn't bloody well good enough." He kicked over a little pile of mud which Tommy had managed to stick together from the debris of sods that had fallen apart in his hands.

"They're awful wet," Michael looked up, fixing his eyes on the white collar and the brown tie, not daring to look into the fat red face, into the malevolent eyes.

"Well if you're not able to foot them, there's a simple solution: you can get out on the road, and don't let me see your arse for the dust rising after you."

Michael felt sick and lonely. He thought of the money he had to earn; he remembered his father's expectations of him; he couldn't get the sack. The trousers of the ganger's grey suit were tucked neatly into a shiny new pair of wellingtons. On the toe of his right wellington was a round wet mark where he had kicked over Tommy's footing.

"Sorry, Mr. Griffin, I'll try to do them better," said Michael meekly.

"You'll bloody well have to do them better," growled the ganger. "And what's more you'll have to go back over every bloody footing that you've done. I want to see them all twice as high as they are."

The ganger stalked off. Michael looked at the footings; they had taken four times as long as usual and now they had to be re-done. He went back to two of the footings and tried to build one on top of the other. They just crumbled underneath the extra weight. He would have to wait and ask his father what to do. Yet he dreaded having to tell him for he still sensed his disappointment of the evening before.

He turned to Tommy who was looking helplessly at his little row of mounds.

"Can't you do them a bit better?" said Michael crossly. "We'll never get this plot done."

"But they won't stay together. They break," explained Tommy.

"Well if you can't do them, go and make the tea. If you're no use on the bog you'll have to stay at home."

When his father came in the evening, Michael told him all that the ganger had said. He hoped that he would be angry and curse the ganger and the other people and even him: but no, his father was silent and the only reaction he showed was one of hurt. Michael asked him what they should do, but he didn't reply. Without taking his tea, he started to work on the top of the plot, taking the footings apart, enlarging the base and building them higher. Michael followed suit. Tommy was about to join them when his father motioned him to sit down where he was.

They spent that evening going over the previous evening's work. All the while his father never spoke to Michael, and at the usual time they gathered up their coats and bags and went home.

Two days later all the plots in their vicinity were finished and the people had moved on. Michael and Tommy were alone and they were still only half-way through the plot. However, Michael was relieved in so far as the ganger would have to move with the new work and would have little opportunity of coming back to check on them. Sure enough they didn't see a ganger for the next three days and by that time they had the plot done. It had taken them just over a week.

It was late in the afternoon when Michael and Tommy again walked down the trench; it took them half an hour to reach the place where the people were now working. When they arrived at the first vacant plot Michael examined it thoroughly. He was determined not to be caught out again. It was poor, though not as bad as the one he had just finished. He examined the plot after that and saw that it was very good.

"Come on," said he to Tommy and he climbed over the turf clamp. When he got to the other side he unpacked the bag and sent Tommy to make the evening tea.

Every five minutes Michael peeped over the clamp to see if the plot was taken. After some time he saw a man coming down along the top of the bank. Michael hid again and hoped that the man would take the bad plot. He listened intently; presently he heard the rumble of dry turf as the man came clambering over the clamp. A knowing half-smile, an embarrassed nod, were exchanged. The man opened his bag and began to gnaw at a sandwich.

Michael felt uneasy about peeping over the clamp in the presence of the man. He glanced over at him but there was no sign of him to keep a look-out. At length his impatience overcame him: he stood up pretending to stretch himself. The plot was not yet taken.

He looked up the bog. A woman and two children were coming down along the bank. Michael's pulse beat faster with anticipation. He knew the woman. She was a Mrs. Murphy and she worked on the bog every summer since her husband deserted her. Would she take it?

Crouching down behind the clamp, Michael was breathless with suspense. He listened and waited, and listened. Eventually his curiosity got the better of him. He peeped over at the plot. She had taken it! Michael hopped across the clamp and hurried to grab the next plot.

Theo Dorgan

ECLIPSE

for PM on her birthday, 25 VI 92

She lifts her skirt above her head
And a black disc hangs in heaven

Her chin is over her shoulder & her eyes
Probe deep into the heft of space.

Silent, and almost without breathing
We watch the spray from her flung hair

Hang shocked and still. Ships crawl on the sea,
Sailors ashore in the loud bars are unsettled.

*

We light a candle on the windowsill
For a thread of light from here to over there,

Arachne's line, bent silver with her tears,
Child of the zodiac banished into dark.

*

And slowly our mother lets her skirt fall,
Her wrist leads heavy cloth in a downward arc,

Drawing the black bull forward—
We know that she cannot afford to miss.

Memory packed in his meaty neck,
All that is blood and smoke and pain of pride

In the wide, arrogant sweep of his horns,
The knot of history muscular in his shoulder.

In the steep galleries of shade and fear,
Stars flare as the steel drives home.

*

I cup Arachne's breast, tilt your bright face
To the moon and me, you kiss me for charm

And promise as your legs float up around my waist
And I jet deep and consoling in your womb.

This candleflame gutters in a wind from space,
Tilts left and right, then grips. Downstairs

The sailors are singing and at peace, the air
Is kind, no one at sea tonight will come to harm.

John F. Deane

ASTRONAUTS

They are tinfoil crayfish in free drift
through the underwater world of space;
they walk nonchalantly out on emptiness,
balance on fingertips a factory of steel;

what we miss are the bubbles
rising reassuringly above them and
tying them still to our breathing;
words emanate from them like the words we spoke

in childhood into resonating old tin cans;
further space is black beyond black
and the earth looms bigger and more beautiful
than we had remembered;

ah well, perhaps they will have learned something
and will come back to tell us if they can find the words.
Sometimes this is how I see it—death—
and I am turning slowly in an old-time waltz

outwards, away from camera, in silence;
I am a lexicon, dispersed, debris
among debris or even, for a moment,
a shooting star in somebody's night sky.

Desmond Egan

SKYLARK
(To the memory of Kieran Collins)

so Kieran old pal your fingering of
the most plaintive music
has been interrupted for keeps the whistle has
slid to the floor in this senseless
exposing silence
and no one else can ever
coax from it your tunes

you have walked out the door
the leather jacket the black western hair
taken for granted with that
precise diffident point of view the shy half laugh
just gone   only this time
you will never slip back join us in a corner and
produce when the mood ripens from your breast pocket
a couple of penny whistles no never
play again play play
head to one side out of the way
of the life dancing round the lounge

in notes from the Burren edge the
spirit notes we cannot fully follow
the music beneath the music
tragic hopeful our race moving again in a way in your
spirals knotty interlacings loops and purls of feeling
a skylark over the Irish bogs one
unknowable last time

and now old friend we are left with the pause
to clap when it's too late to call after you
the thanks that never got said to stand in respect
at the true music of what has become your life
sweet as a spring well

put away the whistle I don't want to hear
in death forever my brother I'm saying goodbye

Pádraig J. Daly

DUVET

Knowing my love of comfort, warmth and sleep,
Some friends gave me a great feathery eiderdown
To ease my Winters.

It will take me like Sinbad
Into lands of strange giants and peoples.

I will unfurl it to the wind
And sail like Brendan round half the world.

I will make a cloak of it like Bodach an Chóta Lachtna;
And when I stretch my arms
Kingfishers, wrens and tiny birds of every colour
Will whoosh from under it.

I will make a tent of it,
Stretched on poles as Yahweh stretched the sky.

It will be my sunshade near warm tides,
My bivouac in lands of snow.

I will spread it on the ground like the Roman widow
And build my basilica on top.

I will put it down on swamps
And build a bridge.

I will line my hollow walls with it
And insulate my ceiling.

It will be my meadow of Summer flowers
In dark December,
My noisy cataract, my Comeragh lake.

May the Lord prosper those who gave it,
Fill their mouths with music,
Bathe their bodies in buttermilk.

May their sheep lamb twice each year,
Their hens lay double eggs,
Their cows flood Ballyclough with cream.

It will teach me to think kindly on human hearts;
And on the heart of God
Who covers us always with undeserved kindness.

Thomas Lyden

WORDS THAT SNARL

The ocean is sad
And I drift
And the tongues of philosophers
Ring around the courtyard
Snarling at all these words
No repentance and no gain
The dust sticks and the gossips
           move on
Eyes closed at the dinner table
Your legacy is your vision
And flickering conversation
Doubts truth at sundown
In your jagged mind you see
Vanished and embracing
A stone left on the boreen
And ghosts ruin the daydream
The confusion turns to gallantry
Brainwashed whispers shiver
Swallowed beneath some burden
Insensitive individuals sneak away
Poetry unwinds like an unhappy pup
Something makes you bleed
It must be your antenna

Flora Joyce

THE FOOD WE'LL EAT IN ONE HUNDRED YEARS TIME

Two thousand and ninety five,
That's a very long way away
But it will be here some day
And what kind of food will we eat by then?
No cows, no sheep, no battery hen
On which to feast, to make our meal
No poor little calves to serve as veal.

We might eat green sludge,
And little red spheres
And of course the potato
Till it comes out our ears
But there's something wrong
I can't quite see what
The potatoes we're eating
Are all covered in spots,
Some pink, some blue, others purple and yellow
Just think what that might do to a fellow!
You could get a tummy ache or some nasty disease
From eating chemical sprayed green peas.

Do you want to know why we're eating this food;
Not to explain would seem a bit rude,
It's because all the animals are no longer alive,
They're gone to the big abattoir up there in the sky.

We took them for granted,
The forests nearly went too

But now they're replanted,
We have paper and glue.

It's a pity the animals didn't get a share,
It's their world too,
It just doesn't seem fair
That they should be kept
In such dark smelly places
With knives and such things being flashed in their faces.

First take the hen
Its sole purpose for eggs,
It has been debeaked
And has a disease in its legs
Do you know why this is?
Do you know what it's from?
It's from being kept in a cage
All day and night long.

And then there's the cow.
Yes, it's mistreated too
It's kept for the milk
And the meat and the glue.

The sow in its crate,
Just tied to one spot
Just suckling and eating,
Such is their lot.

And then there's the sheep.
The nice woolly sheep.
But not skipping in the fields
Like in Little Bo Peep.

They're all crammed into lorries,
Just any old way
It doesn't really matter
So long as farmers get their pay.

Oh let's give them credit,
they really do care,
But not about the animals,
How they're going and where!

Just as long as the money
Gets into their hands
They don't care if the animals
Are squashed up in cans.

As always, of course,
there are a few
Who really do care
But it just won't do.
We want all the farmers
to help keep them alive,
Or they'll really be gone in a hundred years time.

It's really insane, it's cruel, it's preposterous
The commercial farmers have started on the ostriches.
They are kept outside in all kinds of weather
To be killed later on
for their meat
And their feathers.

They're put into a pen
Where pluckers gather round
To rip out their feathers
And bring them to the ground.

Support animal welfare,
It can do you no harm.
Help the animals out of the factory
And back to the farm.

It's really a matter over which
We can't quibble.
We all have so much
And gave them so little.

Gerald Dawe

THE WATER TABLE
(for Tom & Julie Kilroy)

The house is floating on water—
rain-water, seepage off fields,
rivers, thaw, the eventual sea.
Maybe we're all floating.

The house moored like a boat
in this one particular place
sways through days and nights
when we're glued to the t.v.

The water table's rising. Soon
typewriter and microwave,
chairs, teapots, family-pictures
will float up into the trees

and come to rest, like offerings
around a holy well, glistening.
I have seen the ground swell
and foundation cracks settle.

Brian Friel

MAKING HISTORY

O'NEILL: I'm remembering Sir Henry Sidney and Lady Mary, may they rest in peace. We spent the winters in the great castle at Ludlow in Shropshire. I've few memories of the winters. It's the summers I remember and the autumns, in Kent, in the family seat at Penshurst. And the orchards; and the deerpark; and those enormous fields of wheat and barley. A golden and beneficent land. Days without blemish. Every young man's memories. And every evening after dinner Sir Henry would propose a topic for discussion: Travel—Seditions and Troubles—Gardens—Friendship and Loyalty—Good Manners—The Planting of Foreign Countries. And everyone round the table had to contribute—the family, guests, even myself, even his son Philip who was younger than I. And Sir Henry would tease out the ideas and guide the conversation almost imperceptibly but very skilfully so that by the time we rose from the table he had moulded the discourse into a well-rounded and formal essay on whatever the theme was. I was only a raw boy at the time but I was conscious not only that new ideas and concepts were being explored and fashioned but that I was being explored and fashioned at the same time. And that knowledge wasn't unflattering. Drake was there once, I remember. And Frobisher and his officers on the eve of their first South American voyage. Gross men; vain men. But Sir Henry's grace and tact seemed to transform all that naked brutality and imperial greed into boyish excitement and manly adventure. He was the only father I ever knew. I was closer to him and to Lady Mary than I was to O'Hagan who fostered me. I loved them both very much. Anyhow, time came to come home. I was almost seventeen then. And the night before I left Lady Mary had an enormous farewell dinner for me—there must have been a hundred guests. And at the end of the meal Sir Henry got to his feet—I knew he was slightly drunk, maybe he was more drunk than I knew—and he said: 'Our disquisition tonight will explore a matter of some interest to England and of particular interest to Master O'Neill who goes home tomorrow to become a leader of his people. And the matter is this, and I quote from a letter I have just received from my friend, Andrew Trollope. "Those Irishmen who live like subjects play but as the fox which when you have him on a chain will seem tame; but if he ever gets loose, he will be wild again." So. Speak to that, Fox O'Neill.'

And then he laughed. And everybody joined in. And then a hundred people were laughing at me . . .

I left the next morning before the household was awake. And ever since—up until this minute—ever since, that trivial little hurt, that single failure in years of courtesy has pulsed relentlessly in a corner of my heart. Until now. And now for no reason that pulse is quiet and all my affection for Sir Henry returns without qualification. (Pause.) But all that is of no interest to anybody but myself.

Tom MacIntyre

OPEN HEARTH

Peeler-size, Eduardus Rex,
still warm from the blaze :
Pat The Yankee lugged home
the tongs like a bad debt.

The Yankee moved on. The tongs
fell to a rogue blacksmith,
furnished his long left arm.
They sowed the blacksmith in time.

Up on thirty years
the tongs lay propped in a shed,
summer a squeak of swallows,
winter slavish, slavish out.

Wrist supple over turf and scantling,
my love now plies the tongs,
touch, stroke, stir, nudge,
silken endearments, then fire.

Francis Harvey

THE BLACK SHEEP

Listen. The Angelus bell has begun
to toll faintly in the glen. And look,
over there under a low sky bloated with rain,
a man mending fences who takes off his cap
to no one but God and to eat and sleep,
has suddenly bared his head to pray.
Two dogs lie prostrate like acolytes at his feet.
I know his name and the names of his dogs and
once I broke bread with him in the kitchen of
a womanless house as bare and white as
the limewashed house of his God down the road.
We talked about ewes and wethers and how
he'd been searching for a black sheep he'd lost.
I remember the coil of rusted barbed wire
sitting on the bald skull of a boulder like
a crown of thorns encrusted with dried blood and
the ragged cross on the side of his hill was
the skeleton of a flayed scarecrow marking
the place where a crop had failed and he gave in.
And I remember too how he and his dogs
penned me in a corner of that windswept
kitchen like a sheep that had strayed from
the fold of the crucified Sheepman hanging
like a scarecrow from a nail in the wall.

Joan McBreen

ON HEARING MY DAUGHTER PLAY 'THE SWAN'

(from 'The Carnival of the Animals' by Saint-Saens)

My daughter plays Saint-Saens. It is evening
and spring. Suddenly I am outside
a half-opened door. I am six years old
but I already know there's a kind
of music that can destroy.

My mother is playing a waltz, Chopin,
and everything is possible. There are lilacs
in a vase on the hall table, white among
the colourful umbrellas, folded,
full of the morning's light rain.

My sisters' voices are calling one another
far down the street. There are wind-blown leaves
under my father's feet as he enters the room.
I look at him as if for the first time
and he grows old.

I see my mother rise from the piano
and close it gently. She takes a glass
from the table. It is empty. But she has put
a weight in me, the weight of something
that has died in her.

As my daughter sustains the melody
with her right hand, the tumult
of the chords she uses with her left hand
brings into the room
the hush and roar of the sea.

Moya Cannon

HUNTER'S MOON

There are perhaps no accidents,
no coincidences.
When we stumble against people, books, rare moments
out of time,
these are illuminations,
like the hunter's moon that sails tonight in its high clouds,
casting light into our black harbour,
where four black turf boats
tug at their ropes,
hunger for the islands.

Nuala Ó Faolain
CIRCLE OF FEAR

There has been a patronising tone to some of the British reviews of the film of Maeve Binchy's *Circle Of Friends*, whereas the same film has been warmly and comprehensively praised here. "A wonderful sense of period," almost every Irish critic has said. But what is meant by that? Is it just the frocks and the Morris Minors that impress? Is not the absence of any serious analysis of what she chooses to say about the recent past, just another way of patronising her?

She is dismissed as a charming Paddy. Or as the writer of mere novelettes for women. And, of course, her great theme is indeed the central one of popular writing by and for women—the finding of a proper mate. But a comparison between the book and the film of *Circle Of Friends* makes clear again that there is a tough centre to her softness. She is a truth-teller, even if she serves up the truth so well wrapped in humour that readers, it seems to me, are reassured by her moral purpose on a subliminal, not conscious, level.

The film of *Circle Of Friends* is short and simplified and necessarily leaves out much of the context of the book. Which helps to make it evident that at her full length she is not interested in boy-meets-girl in any conventional way. She never fades out on a clinch. What she is interested in is social stability. Her novels generally end with a community—young lovers included—which was temporarily deranged by passion of one kind or another, being most satisfyingly restored to order and health, by disposition of the author. When you strip those wider genialities away, as the film does, her romances are revealed as most uncompromisingly unromantic.

Maybe it's the times she sets them in. *Circle Of Friends* might well distress as much as amuse those who were young before the pill or anything else, when innocence and ignorance could hardly be told apart. The film brings into the light the kind of emotional and sexual detail that academic social historians hardly bother with.

The burden, for example, that young women carried at a time when their own and their young mens hormones impelled them towards intercourse, yet contraceptives were not available. And could not be mentioned, even if they could be got: shyness and shame made friendly communication between attracted young people almost impossible. For a respectable girl to get pregnant was worse than death. Nan in *Circle of Friends* has no option but to betray Bennie and Jack when she gets pregnant: no friendship weighed in such a crisis.

The cad Nan is pregnant by offers to pay for an abortion. "But I'm a Catholic!" she says. This is the hardest thing for people who are young now to accept—that there was a time when sexually active people struggled with inner and outer religious monitors. "I liked the film," a smart young woman said to me, "but all that stuff about bad thoughts and mortal sins—that was all rubbish."

She seemed to think Maeve Binchy put the Catholicism in just to provide an element of farce. But girls did try terribly hard to be good.When they failed, boys despised them for not being good.But if they didn't go some way towards not being good, they might not get a boy at all. And you had to get a boy, so as to marry.

This seems hilarious, apparently, to the modern audience. So do the double standards of the time—presented, as they are by Maeve Binchy, with the equivalent of a beam on her face. The cinema falls about today when one of the girls grudgingly says to her boyfriend, after losing a game of draughts: "I'll hold it. But I won't jiggle it about". But those bargains struck by couples weren't all that funny. The groaning heaps at parties: the cars full of panting fights over hands in bras and on thighs; the dances...

David Lodge's new novel *Therapy* also goes back to the 'Fifties, to a boy who only gets his hands on his Catholic girlfriend during slow waltzes. "Dancing meant," Lodge's narrator says, "that even in a church youth club you were actually allowed to hold a girl in your arms in public... Of course you had to pretend that this wasn't the point of it, you had to chat about the weather or the music or whatever while you steered your partner around the floor, but the licence for physical sensation was considerable. Imagine a cocktail party where all the guests are masturbating while ostensibly preoc cupied with sipping white wine and discussing the latest books and plays, and you have some idea what dancing was like for adolescents in the early 1950s..."

Who else but Maeve Binchy has cared to chronicle that milieu?Where religion and sex were counter-forces, themselves held in check by the third great force of class distinction? Again, this is something you see the more clearly because the film gets it subtly wrong. The Americans who play Jack and Bennie could hardly be more charming. But there isn't space to establish that he's not just a sweet idiot—that he's a hero, as a big doctor's son, to insist that a culchie draper's daughter is the one for him.

Americans are such democrats. They wouldn't believe the intricacies of the snobbery Maeve Binchy understands so well. But neither would they believe—which is true—that students in Dublin c. 1960 were not spotless and perfectly groomed. They were poor, and damp, and there were no showers in their homes. They had just emerged from a school system which did little for their self-esteem. They did not have the confident body-language of the young actors in Circle Of Friends.

Popular writers are very important. Maeve Binchy's accounts of pre-contemporary Ireland are the only ones available to the mass audience—previously an almost all-female audience I'd say, but increasingly, through television and film, a general audience. And she is up to something quite strange. Like Roddy Doyle, she does not baulk at the local social savageries. But she's even more determined than he is to make the sad and the savage funny. The gap between matter and manner is shown up in the new film. It's much too interesting a paradox to patronisingly dismiss.

Mary O'Malley

AT THE BLESSED WELL

Beyond the end of the road
Where only hungry sheep and pilgrims
Know what lies between them
And the grey Atlantic
Two stone mounds mark time.

Earnest at thirteen
In her thin dress and thick coat
She shivered off her shoes.
Her feet shrivelled and turned
A faint blackberry blue
On the thirteenth of November.

Seven circles, sure, slow
As each one joined she threw
A stone into the well. The shale
Gleamed with frost and pennies
From people who had nothing
Lay greening on holy ground
But the well, they said
Was always warm and often cured.

She circled seven times, certain
Of her saint. Little bracelets
Of ripples edged the water.
Below the sea raged.
Her feet on fire she told
Prescribed prayers for fortitude
Deliverance and a happy death.

Rebelling at the last station
She risked it all and begged Cailin
For a little palace in the sun,
The kind that nestles between the covers
Of her hundred and one nights.

The seventh stone dropped in.
It disappeared like a confessed sin.
Cleansed, she ran up the jagged hill.
It's not cold, not cold at all
She called, determined for a miracle.

Seamus Heaney

SAINT KEVIN AND THE BLACKBIRD

1

And then there was Saint Kevin and the blackbird.
The saint is kneeling, arms stretched out, inside
His cell, but the cell is narrow, so

One turned-up palm is out the window, stiff
As a crossbeam, when a blackbird lands
And lays in it and settles down to nest.

Kevin feels the warm eggs, the small breast, the tucked
Neat head and claws and, finding himself linked
Into the network of eternal life,

Is moved to pity: now he must hold his hand
Like a branch out in the sun and rain for weeks
Until the young are hatched and fledged and flown.

2

And since the whole thing's imagined anyhow,
Imagine being Kevin. Which is he:
Self-forgetful or in agony all the time

From the neck on out down through his hurting forearms?
Are his fingers sleeping? Does he still feel his knees?
Or has the shut-eyed blank of underearth

Crept up through him? Is there distance in his head?
Alone and mirrored clear in love's deep river
"To labour and not to seek reward," he prays,

A prayer his body makes entirely
For he has forgotten self, forgotten bird
And on the riverbank forgotten the river's name.

Gabriel Fitzmaurice

THE TEACHER
for David Mason

I wish away my life until the pension
Hoping that, just once, I will connect
With sympathy that is beyond attention;
Instead I keep good order, earn respect.
Once I had a vision for my village—
I'd bring to it a gift of poetry;
Tonight the talk's of quotas and of tillage
And how the barmaid gives out beer for free.
And yet, I've not lost hope in my own people
My vision was at fault; these people need
To sing and dance, get drunk below the steeple
That accuses them of gossip and of greed.
I mind their children, give them right of way
Into a world I've seen and try to say.

Richard Murphy

WALKING ON SUNDAY

Walking on Sunday into Omey Island
  When the tide had fallen slack,
I crossed a spit of wet ribbed sand
  With a cold breeze at my back.

Two sheepdogs nosed me at a stile,
  Boys chevied on the green,
A woman came out of a house to smile
  And tell me she had seen

Men digging down at St. Fechin's church,
  Buried in sand for centuries
Up to its pink stone gable top, a perch
  For choughs and seapies.

I found a dimple scalloped from a dune,
  A landing-slip for coracles,
Two graveyards—one for women, one for men—
  Odorous of miracles:

And twelve parishioners probing a soft floor
  To find what solid shape there was
Under shell-drift; seeking window, door;
  And measuring the house.

Blood was returning dimly to the face
  Of the chancel they'd uncovered,
Granite skin that rain would kiss
  Until the body flowered.

I heard the spades clang with a shock
  Inaugurating spring:
Fechin used plug and feather to split rock
  And poised the stone to sing.

He tuned cacophony to make
  Harmony in this choir:
The ocean gorged on it, he died of plague,
  And hawks nested there.

Dermot Bolger

POEM FOR A NEWSPAPER

Imagine this poem boxed
   Among columns of newsprint
      In a paper you have half-read.

This is the night you move
   into your first house.
      How eerie the rooms seem:

Bare light bulbs,
   Strips of unfaded carpet
      Like sunken graves that mark

Where furniture once stood.
   Paint tins have been stacked
      Beside the spare mattress.

Tomorrow new carpets will arrive.
   You finger the tacks and knife,
      Already hearing in your mind

The trundle of a tricycle,
   Bare feet, muffled by underlay,
      Racing to greet you coming home.

It is midnight when you start.
   This poem is your only witness
      As you rip the old carpets up

To make the floorboards your own.
   The house is naked for you to possess her,
      Yet all you can do is lay newspaper down.

II

Decades pass and you will be dead
When somebody lifts those carpets.

The house stripped bare as they glance
Through these lines you half-began,

Trying to fathom your unknown life,
Your thoughts as you worked, through them.

Eamon Grennan

TWO GATHERING

After supper, the sun sinking fast, Kate and I
have come to the shore at Derryinver
to gather mussels. Across cropped grass, rocks,
we walk to the water's edge where low tide
has exposed a cobbling of cobalt blue shells, others
tucked in clusters under a slick fringe
of seaweed. In my wellingtons
I enter shallow water, bending over
and wresting from their native perch
the muddy clumps of molluscs, rinsing them
in salt water that clouds and quickly clears again
as the tide laps, a slow cat, against me, then
pushing my handfuls into the white plastic bag
I've laid out of the water's way on seaweed.
Kate, in sneakers, is gathering hers
off the dry rocks behind me: almost sixteen,
her slim form blossoms in jeans
and a black T-shirt, long hair falling over
as she bends, tugs, straightens with
brimming hands, leans like a dancer
to her white bag, looks out to me and calls
So many! Have you ever seen so many! her voice
a sudden surprise in that wide silence
we stand in, rejoicing—as she always does
and now I must—at the breathless plenitude
of the world, this wondrous abundance
offering itself up to us as if we were masters
of the garden, parts of the plenary sphere
and circle, our bodies belonging
to the earth, the air, the water, fellow
creatures to the secret creatures we gather
and will tomorrow kill for our dinner.

When I bend again—my hands pale groping starfish
under water—it is Kate's own life I fumble for,
from the crickets singing her name
that September afternoon she was born
to the balance she strikes
between separated parents, her passion
for maths, the names of her lost boys,
or the way she takes my arm
when we take a walk on Wing Road
or up the hill from Tully to the cottage. This instant
I can feel her eyes on my bent back, seeing me
standing over my ankles in water, the slow
tide climbing my boots, my cautious
inelastic stepping between elements
when I place the mussels I've gathered
in the bag. And if I turn to look,
I'll see a young woman rising out of sea-rocks, bearing
the salmon and silver air on her shoulders,
her two hands spilling a darkblue arc, about
to take a dancer's step: I hear the muffled clack
of live shells filling her bag.

In our common sphere of silence we're aware
of one another, working together, until
she calls out—Have you seen
their colours? Brown and olive and bright green
and black. I thought they were only navy blue—
delighted by variety, the minute ripple of things
under water or changing in air, the quick patterns,
as if the world were one intricate vast equation
and she relished picking it over, seeing the figures
unfold and in a split surprising second

edge out of muddle into elegant sense, the way
she's explained to me her love of maths
as a journey through multiple views to a moment
of—yes, she said it—'vision', you simply see it
all in place before your eyes: a flowering branch
of impeccable sense; number and grace
shimmering in a single figure; a shard of truth
shining like the head of a new nail
you've just, with one stroke, driven home.

Feeling the drag and push of water, I know it's time
to move and I do, inching backwards, my hands
still scrabbling under rubbery fronds of seaweed
for the mussels' oval stony bulk, their brief
umbilical resistance as I twist them
from their rock, swirl in water, add them
with drippling chill hands to the bag, sensing
the summer dusk falling all over us. Dad, look! A heron!
standing not twenty yards from us
on the hem of the tide: a grey stillness
staring at nothing
then flicking his serpent-neck and beak
into the water and out, taking a single deliberate step
and then on slow opening wings rising and
flap-gliding across the inlet, inland, heavy
and graceful on the air, his legs
like bright afterthoughts dangling. He's so big,
she calls, How does he do it? and across the raw
distance of rock and water I call back,
It's the span of his wings, he uses the air,
thinking about question and answer, the ways
we're responsible to one another, how we
use our airy words to lift us up

above the dragging elements we live in
towards an understanding eloquent and silent
as blood is or the allergies I've handed
to her system—our bodies' common repugnance
to penicillin, sulfa—all the buried codes
that bind us in a knot even time
cannot untangle, diminishing, in a way,
the distance between us. Did you see, I hear my voice,
his legs? The way they dangled ? Thin—her voice
comes back to me—as sticks, and the colour
of pearl. Funny the way he tucked them in,
putting them away, and she drops a castanet
handful of mussels into her bag.
                                                    My hands
are blueish, a small breeze riffles the water,
the spur of land we're on is drowned
in shade: we've gathered enough
and it's time to go. She watches me wading
through bright, light-saving pools, reaches
a helping hand when I clamber up rock
above the line of seaweed where she stands waiting
on grass the sheep have bitten to a scut,
their tidy shit-piles of black pellets
scattered all over. With pleasure we behold
the two bulging bags I've draped
in glistering layers of olivebrown bladderwrack,
both of us thinking of the dinner we'll have
tomorrow: brown bread, white wine, a green
salad, the steaming heaps of open shellfish
—ribboned in onion, carbuncled
with chunks of garlic—the plump dull-orange
crescent of each one gleaming
in its mottled shell, sea-fragrance curling off
the greybright salty peppered soup

they've offered up to us, and in it the brilliance
of lemon wedges swimming. At least once each summer
we have a family feast like this, and I picture
her delight in the dipping of buttered bread, laying
a hot mussel on her tongue, the squirt of sea-tang and
flesh
against her teeth, sipping the wine that's still
a stranger to her palate, remembering
the way the sun went down behind the two of us
as we gathered dinner, as if our lives
were always together and this simple.

                                              Now
we stand side by side for a minute or two
in silence, taking the small bay in and the great shade
spreading over sea and land: across the water,
on a sloping headland of green fields, we see
how a stopped hand of sunlight still
in the middle distance lingers, brightening
one brief patch of ground with uncanny light
so I cannot tell if I'm looking at a moment past
of perfect knowledge, or a bright future
throbbing with promise. Then Kate
is giving me, again, her words: I wonder
will it strike us over here, is what
I hear her say—her words, unanswered,
hanging between us as we turn to go.

Paula Meehan

ROSSADILLISK AUBADE

It is the breaking hour.
The sun has already opened
Dublin, London, Istanbul
And beyond until the East ends.

It will lighten our skylight window soon;
It will steal all the silver stars from the loft.
I slide from the warm banglet of your arms
To make this day my own.

It struggles over the Twelve Pins
To startle Cleggan into the staring morning
Like a bird astonished by the beat of its wings.
It rustles the seamen and traders
From their secret sea haunted pillows.
It sets a hundred young dogs on phantom postmen.
It plucks Inishbofin out of the dark
And mounts her crystal on the green ocean.
It nudges the Kings' wiry heifers down
The primrose daubed long acres
That lead only to the waves.

You will be still in the moon world
Lost in old arms that have held you
Or the new ones you have yet to name
While the sun clears the rim of the mountain
That rhymes with the tossing sea
That rhymes with your sea scarred eyes.

Ross Cottage, Rossadillisk,
March 1981

Frank McGuinness

OUR LADY OF KYLEMORE ABBEY

I appeared out of purdah on this mountainside,
A statue overlooking the lake at Kylemore, White
And hard faced. They called me the mother of God, as if
He needed a mother, as if I needed a God.

There are those who wonder about my present position.
A woman suspended on a pedestal. I don't like it
But it's a living, and it beats what I used to do.
This involved melting the salt from the sea,

Writing the Bible in the salt so distilled, dipping
The parchment in fresh water and giving solace
To men who weep, to women giving birth to a mountain.
Mercy made me Our Lady Of Kylemore Abbey.

From that day on though, I lost all heart, all interest,
Receiving the worship of lonely girls, rowing in the lake,
Girls like myself once, waiting for husbands to sail
Into fertile places. They never arrived, these husbands—

They had wives at home to conquer. Yet I loved
The smell of their ships. They caught fish, I fire,
And used it to burn their boats. They drowned then in the
        arms
Of other women. My husbands dead, I went into purdah

And veiled my face, Our Lady of Kylemore Abbey.
I dressed in this white and gave to the poor.
I gave them the mercy that once hardened me
When I was raw and awkward but full of grace.

John Morrow

THE MEM-SAHIB

It began with an incident that her friends back home would call 'Pure Samantha', meaning a fusion of self-righteous wrath and high drama that only someone normally as charming as she could get away with without appearing downright vulgar.

There had been many such incidents in the past—well chronicled, for there always seemed to be sympathetic witnesses to hand when they occurred, witnesses guaranteed to retail details across dinner tables for months afterwards. This one, Samantha knew, would get back to Sevenoaks and environs via her daughter Kim, over from University for the Easter break.

This awareness of social notoriety was, of course, part and parcel of Samantha's charm. Another aspect of that charm was that the incidents usually took place in the context of her various enterprises. The time, for instance, when she had dramatically exposed the Masonic-like twitchings and winkings of an antique dealer's ring at a country house auction near Hove; or when, free-lancing in interior decoration, she had tongue-lashed a Union official who had been attempting to organise her 'help', all of whom were 'doing the double'.

Back home in England, the social circle in which she moved consisted mostly of the families of senior Civil Servants or minor politicians—her husband, Philip, had been a Principal in the Home Office and now held a similar position to do with law and order in Northern Ireland. In this strata of comparative affluence, most of the wives found the chores of being a social secretary cum hostess onerous enough, and the few who did carry on a separate career did so in, say, the elegant end of estate agency; only Samantha worked always at the sharp end, the market place, where moved vaguely shady characters involved in the thriving 'black economy' of the competitive 'eighties. Most admired in her the brash energy required to swim in that nether-world; a few others spoke scathingly of her having inherited the morés of a used-car salesman, a reference to her father having owned one of the largest car franchises on the south coast.

Samantha had not wanted to come to Northern Ireland. Besides the facts of Kim at University and Roger at Rugby, there had been the imminence of her partnership with an outcast from the Triad Society in a Chinese Takeaway business in Purley, an enterprise fraught with all kinds of hazard and good for a positive rash of 'pure Samantha' cameos. The hazards of life as the wife of a senior British official in Northern Ireland had not entered into her thinking. At the time of the incident in question they were well into their second year and Philip, always reticent about official matters, had not yet revealed to her the circumstances of his sudden exile. Her decision to accompany him had been dictated solely by a feeling that now as never before Philip needed the support of a home, a base.

But Samantha had quickly become bored with the base, and boredom for Samantha always presaged a fresh business venture (boredom, not money: a Trust Fund and the sale of Daddy's franchise had seen to that). All of which was why, on a blustery April day one week before opening date, Samantha was busy with mops and brushes clearing up the mess left by workmen who had installed the huge oven in what was to be 'The Godfather's Pizza Parlour, Takeaway and Express Delivery'. Outside the prime corner site in one of the dormitory towns along the coast of Belfast Lough, a short, fat, red-faced man teetered on top of a ladder.

"He's drunk," said Kim.

"He's always drunk," said Mrs. McCracken.

"Drunk or sober, he's the only signwriter available," said Samantha.

Kim and Mrs. McCracken, Samantha's daily woman, were lending a hand. At 20, Kim had the makings of her mother's dark good looks, but without the flash and temperament that had led to Samantha, during her brief dabble in the Higher Education, to be nicknamed 'Gypsy'.

A burst of song from the top of the ladder caused Kim and Mrs. McCracken to look at one another meaningfully, Mrs. McCracken sighing, tutting and tittering in her mildly insane Irish way. Samantha's response was to say: "As long as he carries out my instructions he can dance a jig for all I care."

"Pretty vague instructions, I'd say," said Kim sullenly.

Samantha's reply was gauged to be irritatingly bright. "Oh, I don't know, dear. 'Godfather' equals 'Italian Gangster'. That drunk little artist and I are around the same vintage, so we talked about George Raft and Edward G. Robinson and came to a rough compromise. The only 'musts' are a moustache and a snap-brimmed hat."

"Marlon Brando played the Godfather," stated Kim.

"I know that, dear. But the little man told me he hasn't seen a film since 1963."

"The same fella hasn't seen anything but the bottom of a pint glass since 1963," said Mrs. McCracken dryly. "If you don't mind me asking, Missis," she went on, "what put you in mind of the Godfather thing?"

"I don't at all mind you asking, Mrs. McCracken," cried Samantha, for all the world like a remedial teacher pleased that a backward child was 'showing interest'. "You see, quite recently the American authorities discovered that organised criminals were using a chain of Pizza parlours as a cover for their underworld activities. It got a lot of publicity in the press and TV over here, and I do think that people are attracted by just a hint of the illicit, if only by association. Don't you think so, Mrs. McCracken?"

Mrs. McCracken was heard to mutter: "Ah well, I suppose there's Godfathers and Godfathers." But Samantha did not have the opportunity to inquire as to the meaning of this strange utterance. At that moment the artist appeared inside the front door, wiping paint-stained hands on his paint-stained stomach. "We're coming along nicely, Missis," he reported, touching the peak of his flat cap with a forefinger. "And I was wondering about the prospects of a wee bit of an advance. It's very thirsty work up there." He grinned roguishly.

"Is it indeed," said Samantha briskly, "let's see how nicely you've got on before we make any rash decisions."

She and Kim went into the street and looked up. By any standards he had not got on very well. A faint outline of letters and nothing at all that looked like George Raft or Edward G. Samantha's verbal assault on the little man was shrill and Anglo-Saxon, sending an embarrassed Kim running back into the shop. At first he blustered— "No woman's gonna talk to me like that"— but when she kept on talking to him like that, and worse, he wilted; and when she swore that if he wasn't finished that day he could whistle for his money, he climbed the ladder resignedly, parched— but not beaten by a long chalk.

It was twilight when he finished. Surveying his handi-work, Samantha, mellowed by a couple of pre-prandial gins, said that his Godfather looked more like a Greek chef than an Italian gangster, but that he had got the hat right. She also complimented him on the creative addition of a scar on the right cheek-bone. Scarface: a nice dramatic touch, she thought. The artist snatched the notes from her hand and started running for the nearest pub, shouting incomprehensible curses over his shoulder. Mrs. McCracken, passing out of the shop on her way home, looked up at the frontage, muttered "Oh Holy God!" and scuttled away.

That was the last they saw of Mrs. McCracken. For the next two days they phoned her home repeatedly without success. In that time Kim fancied she detected in passers-by a curious, almost furtive, interest in the shop. Samantha was delighted, say-ing that any interest was good interest, and she accused Kim of watching too many horror videos.

On the afternoon of the third day, when Samantha was alone in the shop, three men entered, though not together. Two came in first, very fit-looking young men, dressed casually, the sort who carry their shoulders as if they were separate entities. They looked around briefly, completely ignoring Samantha and her courteous "What can I do for you, gentlemen?", and then the third man came through the door. He was middle-aged, short and stockily built. He wore a neat dark overcoat and a white choker, a vaguely clerical combination. Samantha noted the abundance of his black greasy-looking hair and wondered where she'd seen him before, convinced that she had. Then her gaze focused on his right cheekbone and she gasped, "Oh my God!"

Scarface grinned widely and said: "Aye, I've just been admiring the painter's wee joke. He's my brother-in-law, so he'll survive it, where many another wouldn't. Still an' all, it's done, and all the gapers of the town have had their fill, so we might as well look to ways of making a profit out of it. That's what has me here"—he signalled his two companions and they exited swiftly out the front door—"I think, Missis, you and me should have a wee talk about business."

He was leaving nearly two hours later, just as Kim arrived. They met briefly in the doorway. Kim's eyes bulged and she pointed a trembling finger at his retreating back. "That's—" she began to say..."That's Mr. Smith, our new partner," cried Samantha, gathering up her bemused daughter in her arms and waltzing around the room singing a song remembered from her teens as a fan of Hollywood musicals: "We're in the money/And skies are sunny/We've gotta lotta what it takes to get around."

And so it seemed in the first three weeks of the Godfather's trading. All branches of the business boomed. It took four additional staff, provided by Mr. Smith, to cope. Orders and people poured in from as far away as the two other dormitory towns along the Loughside. Samantha was so absorbed in the business that she scarcely set eyes on husband Philip in those three weeks, and it was with some annoyance that she received his request, by way of Kim, that they were to have one of their formal dinners together on Friday evening.

Normally, she looked forward to these occasional, very intimate, events. A hired chef and serving-girl; her Daddy's best silver plate, on which were etched the emblems of Rolls-Royce and Bentley; Philip and she in full dress fig. But this time the summons had had a peremptory nuance to it completely out of keeping with the Philip she knew, causing her to approach the evening with some trepidation.

For all that, sitting opposite her suavely handsome husband and relaxing in the almost soporific ambience of his deeply resonant Cambridge vowels, Samantha again tried to detect a trace of the grammar school scholarship boy from Scunthorpe and, finding none, rejoiced for him... Then suddenly, over coffee and liqueurs, he said rather than asked: "You've taken a partner in your latest enterprise," and Samantha knew that her instinct about the evening had been right, they having always preserved a mutual reticence about their affairs.

She replied: "Yes, a Mr. Smith. A local... entrepreneur, I suppose you'd call him."

Philip then astounded her by lighting a cigarette and inhaling deeply, something she hadn't seen him do for over ten years. He said: " A Mr. 'Torchy' Smith, to be precise. My colleagues in Security tell me that his entrepreneurial effort is largely in the realm of real estate, an interest which he developed by the simple but effective means of burning down the premises of an opposing faction and acquiring the vacant sites, hence the nickname. I should also tell you—and I'm certain you are not aware of this—that the success of your current venture is due to the sudden and mysterious closure of three similar establishments within a radius of ten miles. Now this sort of thing may equate with your idea of the 'free economy', Samantha, but I must tell you that my people, to say the least, are not pleased."

All Samantha could find to say was, "Oh darling, have I landed you in the soup?'
"Again," said Philip, inhaling greedily. "You may not have known it, but the prospect of your becoming involved in a Chinese Tong war in Purley had quite a lot to do with my secondment here... Still," and here he sighed resignedly, "I suppose we

should look on the bright side and hope that Mr. Torchy Smith will prove the cause of our return to civilisation."

Poor Philip. At present he is in the middle of a four year tour in the Falkland Islands. So is Samantha. At dinner tables around Sevenoaks there is talk of a wine bar in Port Stanley called 'The Thatcher', its frontage adorned with a caricature of a well-known imbiber. But it may only be that 'Pure' Samantha, as she'd always hoped, has become a necessary legend.

Máire Mhac an tSaoi

MÁTHAIR NA CÉADGHINE
(Do Susan)

Cuireann an bhunóc ar an gcín
Agus cuireann í féin i leataoibh;

Sleamhnaíonn, fé mar shleamhnaíonn
An fhalaing dá guala síos,
Na cianta cairbreacha siar—

Rángaíonn ré órga arís,
An bhuime dheoil 's an naí,
An bheirt ina haon mar bhí
Ó thús, mar a bheidh de shíor.

Cuireann í féin i leataoibh
Is de chomhartha láimhe foilsíonn
Mistéir agus timpeall na mblian—,

Eágosaint a pearsan treisíonn
Ar dhiamhair a scéimhe—
                              Samhlaím
Gurb' í ráiteas an tsoíscéil í—

Líonann mo shúile, is airím
Fírinne an fhocail ghroí:
'An té ghéilleas a bheatha, slánaíonn!'

John MacKenna

HAIKU CALENDAR

i
Beyond the half-door
could be anything but how
his hands cup her breasts.

ii
The tractor roars and
slows, turning in a spray of
swirling paper gulls.

iii
Soft, ineffective
light. A sky of melted slate
hardens after dark.

iv
In this room it is
silent. Outside. an orange
sliced in smoke, the moon.

v
Lambent, the cherries
drench their heavy breasted heat
in the lingam grass.

vi
So much yellow now—
heartsease; primrose; oxeye. And
in the winter this.

vii
The 'phone continues
silent. Whispering: the past
is an old story.

viii
Helianthin. More
foggy wedding snaps, porches
clipped. Dry, nusty leaves.

ix
Crick. Above my head
laburnum pods split in the
unexpected heat.

x
Jug of yellow flags,
sheet soaked in sweat and seed; rich
languid memories.

xi
Wind on the corner,
teenage coats flap about each
other. Love, oh love.

xii
Frost. Inside the hall,
where logs spat scented light, a
gypsy-haired girl.

Phil MacCarthy

LADY CHATTERLEY

We curled on the stairs
outside 'Sacred Heart',
talking after lights out—

Lawrence, Mansfield,
Virginia Woolf,
our first love.

That world would startle
with nuns on the prowl
or the shock of our voices

become one
like a sudden bright moon
flooding the stairway;

six floors down,
a grandfather clock
in the convent hall

ringing each small hour.
Sleepless bones creak
getting up to leave,

night-gowns we shrug close,
your hair falls blonde on my skin
with whitest touch

placed in my hand,
and beautiful you are gone
leaving me

wordless
on a precipice,
hugging the forbidden book.

James Simmons

SESTINA AT MONS

The Bell-tower off the Avenue des Clercs
in Mons is worn and old and being restored.
Beffroi they call the tower. The scaffolding
hides and protects, preparing it to shine.
In some good future the exterior
will, like the sounding bells, be beautiful.

The spire is gold already, beautiful.
From streets below the visitors and clerks
look up and smile, though the exterior
is blurred by building work. To be restored
requires a dusty interim. The shine
is gilt they carry up the scaffolding.

Before I saw this ugly scaffolding
I heard the bell songs, clear and beautiful,
come in the window with the glow and shine
of morning on the Avenue des Clercs.
The nervous traveller's spirit was restored,
bed-warm, tuned in to that exterior.

Bell-sounds and sunshine was a sweet exterior
internalised in me. The scaffolding
is like the surgery I need to be restored
to health, by pain. I know what's beautiful,
sauntering down The Avenue Des Clercs,
savouring cobbles, watching shop fronts shine.

I woke at six and heard the six notes shine,
and entertained within exterior

sounds of the morning cars, of Belgian clerks
walking to work, men on the scaffolding
rattling sharp tools so that the beautiful
bell-tower of Beffroi could be restored.

If I come back the tower will be restored,
like the cathedral. All of it will shine
like its old self and be more beautiful
than I imagine. My exterior
will have decayed some more. No scaffolding
restores the ageing poets or the clerks.

Welcome us back, our unrestored exteriors,
askew beauty, walking stick scaffolding,
elbow shine, seat of pants shine, poets and clerks.

Fred Johnston

STRANGER

When you speak Irish with her
I am put in my place
I am the stranger looking on

So much for all I know
A Planter's suspicion
Roots itself out from the gut

I sense secrets exchanged
Things said that I
Have no right to overhear

But I hear them
And cannot decipher them
Imagination is a sad scholar

So much for all I know—
This is what I am
An untongued foreigner.

Fred Johnston

DOCKLANDS

"Fios a d'fhionnas ó chlann an duig..."
                    Máirtín Ó Direáin: 'An Stailc'

Docklands were tribal, assured
aloof gantries, cranes under orders
hierarchy of hoist, pulley, steel cable

It closes down, grass in the rails
a shutter flapping out a single chord, a white
bird tossing like a rag in the blue air

And men—I know some of them—bend
against the salted wind, smoke, screw up their
faces, make loser horse-race jokes

Their backs turned to what's sinking
all-hands; no word for all that's gone under,
no need to lock gates on the lost forever.

Fred Johnston

ISLAND

Grey dock under the white sun
I waited for the ferry to come in
And as it did, over it's shoulder
The island slunk back behind sea-haze

Driving with the sea at my right hand
Into a small city of hot stones and salt
Well-walked by Sunday people like myself
Who've left their shadows in some other place.

Anne Le Marquand Hartigan

STILL

The dead await you.
Their cold arms
Their still minds
Are open

Where do my stillborn sisters lie
Orphaned in another's grave?
Did they lay you side by side
Curved, womb moulded naturally ?

Little moon
children,
secure
on a tendril,
you float
tied
to the side
of the world.

Playing
in your warm
dawn,
rocked
by your great
sea mother,
drops,
in her fertile ocean.

Heartbeat
heartbeat

repeat the certainty
of the other.

Pale plantings
your sun
surrounds,
engorged
with plenty
knowing
each shove and showing
touch and tread
in your cosy country.

What   that
sharp   cry
where   beyond
is   there?
Out   there
this   light
night   decending
where sister where
this   downing?
An abyss
an outer space
place?
O no place.

They lay upon the table
they were perfect she said
perfect with hair and shell nails
and tiny eyes. They lay on the table
in the bright light perfect
their toes curled in mild
surprise at being there.

While my mother fought to live
Tempest tossed upon her bed
In another woman's arms
Her sweet fruits were laid to rest.

The gentle dead encompass you
Nothing new can harm or snare
You who never felt a breath
Perfect in the earthing's care.

The dead await you.
Their cold breasts
Their still minds
Are open,
And the earth is blind.

(This poem was written to commemorate my twin still-born sisters who were delivered full term, five years or so before my own birth. I discovered many years later that they were buried in the coffins of other dead persons, somewhere in England.) Immortal Sins, Salmon Poetry.

Michael Viney

THE LOST LANGUAGE OF SWANS

The whooper swans flew in on schedule a couple of weeks ago. For a day or two, as I worked at my desk, my eye was caught by a distant ripple of snowy wings, shining out low against blue sea just above the line of the dunes.

They arrived in threes and fours and half-dozens, swerving in across the duach and becoming suddenly huge above the little dots of sheep. As they vanished into the hollow where the lake is, I made a mental note to go down and pay my respects. The song of the swans is the last wild language of this place and it heralds the wild season, winter, which I love.

I would go at a 'secret' time, just before dawn, and see what, if anything, whooper swans feel about the coming of another day. I have sometimes watched them feeding by moonlight, beaks dripping pondweed and diamonds.

A last sliver of the Hunter's Moon, a bright rim to the darkened disc, hung above Mweelrea to tempt me out at 6 a.m., and then was promptly swallowed by a black shower looming from the sea. Without a flashlamp (by design), I let The Plough lead me through the shallows of the channel, and soft starglow guide me across the strand to the grey plain of the duach.

There are navigation aids here, when you know them: strong black lines across the grass, linking the channel of the tidal lake with other streams and waterways. They have the look of sheep-trails, but the otters were here first, and these are paths they made.

I know where they lead, and chose the one to the lochan on the seaward side of the swans. As I walked, I was trying to sort out the calls of invisible waders in the marsh: curlew and redshank, and something else I didn't know (not snipe: they're very quiet).

Some ducks quacking in the murkiness: they'd be mallard, the females are especially vocal in autumn. Mallard are the first lake-birds to panic and fly, unsettling everything around them. To fool them, I took a detour round the back of the lake-cliff, picking a way up across ribs of rock and squelching through pockets of bog.

The cliff is a precipice clad with ferns and ivy. If you slipped you would fall into a dark scrub of hazel, thorn and mossy boulders; no one would know you were there. This high rampart above the lake, like an overgrown castle wall, gives the swans' music a magical resonance. As I crept forward, crouching, to a flat rock dry enough to lie on, the first, fluting notes drifted up.

Like a flugelhorn, it's said, but that suggests a sound all wind, whereas this has a reed vibrating somewhere in its throat. "Audible at a great distance," says the book, "these sounds are delivered through a specially elongated windpipe." There's a sad little descant of three falling notes and a whole suite of individual buglings, right up to the martial. But it's the gentle, echoing, contrapuntal chords that get you—a Bach variation one doesn't want to end.

At first glance, the lake below seemed empty. Then I found a flotilla of half a dozen whoopers, pale ghosts on pewter ripples. Another 30 were clustered at the marshy end, littered among the rushes like foam or flotsam. Many were sleeping, beaks thrust deep into their back feathers, for warmth; others were grooming. As the light strengthened, I saw ochre stains on necks that had been probing the raw mineral muds of Iceland.

The flotilla turned to face the wind. The calls picked up in strength and pace. Heads were bobbing and nodding—not in unison, exactly, but vigorous consensus. I thought of barnacle geese on the islands, and the subtle flick of white cheeks that they share before the whole flock takes wing. Whooper swans are merely more emphatic.

Taking off or landing, swan flight compels you to watch, mechanics of air and muscle, lift and thrust, all made thrillingly visible and obvious. The six took off in a line, running like sprinters to waken the wind. It bore them up and away in a slow arc over the fields, low over sleeping houses, just about clearing the poles at the bend of the hill.

When I turned the glasses back to the lake, another six swans were out in the middle, fluting in chorus and nodding to go. They took the same, low sweep above the land. The rest slept on peacefully, or continued to preen, their feathers more radiant moment by moment in the golden glow from the clouds.

So that's what happened before breakfast: a dozen wild swans got up and went somewhere. I'm glad I bothered.

Maidhc Dainín Ó Sé

AN CROÍ

I dteanga na Gaolainne agus sa Bhéarla chomh maith is minic a chloisfeá tagairt do chroí an duine. Fear flaithiúil nó bean fhlaithiúil—"nach diail an croí atá aige nó aici." ls dócha gur chualamar an seanrá: "Is mór an trua fear croí mhóir i mbaile mór gan airgead." "Buail bos ar do chroí." Luaitear an croí leis an ngrá. Tóg an t-amhrán breá san in ár dteanga dhúchais Máirín de Barra—"Is ar m'eirí dhom mar maidin, mar do chealg tú an croí ionam."

Is é an croí a bhriseann le brón agus cruatan an tsaoil. Is é an croí, dar linn, a ardaíonn ar chloisint dea-scéal. Dhera, d'fhéadfainn leanúint orm go dtí lá Philib a' Cleite ar an gcuma a scríobhadh riamh ar an gceangal atá idir croí agus colainn an duine.

Bhí sé dlúite isteach im' aigne agus aigne daoine nach mé gurb é an croí istigh sa duine a thug an t-olc nó an mhaith chun cinn ann, an formad nó an tsaint. Ach ar m-anam, caithfeadh a rá go bhfuilim tagaithe ar mhalairt aigne air seo le déanaí.

"Conas a bheadh aon chúntas ag tiománaí leoraí ar an gcroí. Fág anailís dá leithéid fé na dochtúirí, nó eolaithe atá oilte sa chúram san," a deireann tú. "Ní dhéanfad, am baiste! "Is cá bhfuairis an t-eolas?" a cheisteofá. Cuir cluas ar éisteacht agus neosfad duit.

Mo dheartháir Páid a chuaigh ar imirce go Chicago Mheiriceá sa bhliain 1956, fear teann láidir na laethanta úd ab ea é D'oibrigh sé go cruaidh ar na docks ar feadh roinnt blianta, ag láimhseáil earraí trom-mheáchain. Uaireanta ag tabhairt fé'n iomad de bharr fearúlachta agus neamhthuisceana. Níos déanaí chuaigh sé ag tiomáint leoraí. Ualaí feola a bhíodh sé ag tiomáint ó áit go chéile. Bhíodh air cabhair a thabhairt, ag líonadh na n-ualaí agus dá bhfolmhú chomh maith. Is minic a bhíodh air leathchorp beithígh a iompar ar a ghualainn, straidhn nach beag ar an gcroí is righne.

Bhí breis saoráide aige áfach nuair a smaoinigh duine éigin cliste ar an inneall a dtugtar an forklift air. Ach fén dtráth seo bhí an oiread stracaí fachta ag an gcroí gur fhág sé máchaill air.

Sa bhliain 1981 fuair sé taom croí in aois 44 dó. Cuireadh cóir leighis air a dhein maitheas dó. Ach sa bhliain 1988 fuair sé rattle eile. Bhí an taom seo i bhfad ní ba ghéire ná an chéad cheann. Tar éis dó mí a chaitheamh san ospidéal agus gach sórt tástála dá dhéanamh air, chuir an dochtúir in iúl dó go raibh a chroí chomh máchailithe, muna gcuirfí malairt chroí ann, gurb é an bás a bhí i ndán dó go luath. Ach misneach níor thréig riamh Páid. Ar m-anam ach go dtug sé an cead don dochtúir é a chur ar an liosta feithimh chun croí úr a fháil. An fhaid a bhí sé ag feitheamh leis an gcroí fuair sé taom eile a d'fhág sínte ar leabaidh a bháis é. Is cuimhin liom féin go maith a bheith ag propáil chun dul sall go dtí Chicago ar an sochraid.

Gan muinín fágtha ná coinne ag éinne leis, cuireadh in iúl don chlann go raibh croí ar fáil dó, croí le garsún óg a hocht mbliana déag a maraíodh i dtionóisc ghluaisteáin. Buaileadh ar an mbord Páid, le foireann des na dochtúirí croí ab fhearr sna Stáit Aontaithe ag obair air. D'osclaíodar an chliabh agus scoireadar na féitheoga go dtí'na chroí, cheangail suas le hinneall iad agus chuir an croí úr san áit ina mbíodh a chroí féin. Bhí go maith is ní raibh go holc—an croí nua ag déanamh a chúraim ar feadh trí lá. I ndeireadh an triú lae lig an croí úr raid nár cheart dó a dhéanamh. B'shin é an uair a' tuigeadh do na dochtúirí nár oir an croí do chorp Pháid. Bhí orthu é a chur ar an mbord arís, é a oscailt agus an croí san a bhaint as. Cheap a chlann agus na dochtúirí san áireamh go raibh a phort seinnte, mar bhí sé ag brath ar inneall in ionad an chroí chun é a choimeád ina bheatha. Thug Páid a hocht lá dhéag ceangailte don inneall ag feitheamh le croí eile. Bhí na dochtuirí réidh chun an t-inneall a chur de nuair a fuaireadar croí eile dó—fear bliain is fiche a maraíodh de rothar gluaiste nuair a bhuail sé falla. Cuireadh an croí i bhfearas in ucht Pháid. Thug sé seachtain gan chasadh gan chorraí, gan ghíog ná míog as. Is é a bhí na dochtuirí in amhras gurb amhlaidh a bhí sé rófhada ar an inneall agus ar a shon go raibh an croí úr ag bualadh go rithimiúil, go raibh a chorp róthráite sara bhfuair sé an croí.

Ach fág fén Éireannach é. Ar an seachtú lá d'oscail sé a shúile agus d'fhéach ina thimpeall. Bhuel, thosnaigh sé ag gibris gur scanraigh sé an bhanaltra a bhí ar diúité. Ghlaoigh sí ar an dochtúir. Thugadar uair a chloig ansiúd ag iarraidh a dhéanamh amach cad a bhí Páid ag rá. Ar deireadh thiar thall, sea, bhí an dochtúir ag admháil gur tharla suaitheadh éigint mínádúrtha dá chorp nuair a cuireadh an croí eile ina chliabh. Dúirt sé ná feaca sé riamh ón gcéad lá a chuir Dochtúir Bearnard an chéad chroí úr sa duine a leithéid ag tarlú. Am baiste! Bhí glaochanna gutháin ag dul siar is aniar trasna an Domhain ó dhochtuir amhain go dtí dochtuirí eile ag iarraidh an scéal a réiteach. Sea, ní raibh faic fágtha ach fios a chur ar an gclann agus an scéal a chur féna mbráid.

Chuaigh beirt iníon Pháid, Máire Áine agus Terry, go dtí an t-ospidéal agus mo dheartháir Dónal lena gcois. Isteach sa bharda leo. Tá's aige Dia féin, ach go raibh mo dhuine istigh agus é ag caitheamh thairis fós. "Could any of you tell us," arsa an dochtúir, "What is he cackling about? Or has the medical profession tapped into the twilight zone?"

Phléasc mo dheartháir, Dónal, amach ag gairí. Chuir sé in iúl don dochtúir agus don mbanaltra go raibh Páid ag labhairt ina theanga dhúchais, an Ghaolainn. Nuair a ceistfíodh Dónal ar cad a bhí ar bun aige. "Tá ag cur in iúl dá athair go bhfuil sé ag dul suas go Cam a' Lochaig ag triall ar phota móna. Bhuel, ba bhreá sásta a bhí an dochtúir é sin a chloisint. "He is reaching into his subconscious mind," ar sé. Nach diail an t-eolas a tháinig go dtí an dochtúir de gheit?

An fhaid a bhí Páid ag teacht chuige féin san ospidéal, creid é nó ná créid, bhí air Béarla d'fhoghlaim arís. Ach nár gheall le sampla é, d'fhan teanga an chliabháin leis. Thóg sé leathbhliain uaidh teacht chuige féin. Nuair a thugas féin turas ar Chicago ansan tamall ó shin, chuireas an cheist chuige: nuair a bhí sé ar leabaidh a bháis, an bhfuair sé a bheag nó a mhór ar an dtaobh eile? "Béal an gheata, sin uile, agus bhí bolta dúbalta air," d'fhreagair sé le leathgháire ar a aghaidh. Dheineas dian-scrúdú ar gach pioc dá iompar. Is é ba mhó a bhí ag déanamh mearbhaill dom, nuair a tóg tar croí as corp amháin agus é a chur isteach i gcorp eile, an dtugann an croí sin leis aon pháirt de bhéasa nó iompar an choirp a d'fhag sé.

Sea, thugas coicíos le cois Pháid, dá fhaire go géar gach cor agus cúinne a chas sé, gach greim a d'ith sé. An mbíodh sé ag sranntarnaigh ina chodladh? Bhuel, caithfead a rá nár thaibhsigh aon athrú sa bhfear domhsa. B'é an fear céanna é a d'fhág Carachán tríocha éigin bliain roimis sin—na geáitsí céanna ar a bhéal nuair a bhíonn sé ag ithe. An t-aon athrú beag amháin ar thógas ceann de áfach, gach uair a gheobhadh cailín óg thar bráid a bheadh go híseal sna ficheadaí, do chasfadh a cheann agus do leanfadh í le spreang ina shúile. Ach ansan dá ngeobhadh bean thar bráid a bheadh níos congaraí dá aos féin, shuífeadh sé ansiud
chomh neamhairdiúil agus darb é madra na gcomharsana a gheobhadh thar bráid.

"Ó fuairis an croí úr", a cheistíos, "An ndein sé aon difríocht duit?" "Dhera, cad atánn tú ag rá, a dhuine," ar sé agus fuinneamh ina chuid cainte. "Dhein agus é. Anois aon uair a chím cailín óg dathúil, bíonn fonn orm í a leanúint, go dtí an altóir dá mba ghá." "Ní foláir gurb é croí Casanova a fuairis," arsa mise. "N'fheadar, am baiste! Ach raghad lena chois go haon áit a thabharfaidh sé mé. Ná beinn marbh gan é." Chuireas an cheist thubaisteach chuige: "An cuimhin leat ó d'óige go dtí an lá atá inniú ann?" "Is cuimhin. Ach thóg sé cúpla bliain uaim tar éis na hobráide na píosaí a chur le chéile. Is mé an fear céanna inniú agus nuair a d'fhágas broinn mo mháthar."

Riamh ó thána abhaile ón dturas go dtí Chicago, táim ag meascadh agus ag meas an scéil i mo cheann agus táim tagaithe don dtuairim nach é croí an duine a mhúnlaíonn agus a rialaíonn cosán ná cás an duine, agus mar a dúirt mé ar dtus, níl baint ag an gcroí le fáilte, flaithiúlacht ná saint an duine—ach gurb é an inchinn a rialaíonn agus a bhfuil máistreacht aige ar an duine. Sea, mar sin, conas a déarfad an seanfhocal? "Is mór an trua fear inchinne móire i mbaile mór gan airgead." "Buail bos ar d'inchinn."

"Tut! Tut! Tut! a Mhaidhc Dainín! Is cuma fén méid taighde atá déanta agat ar an gcroí. In ainm Dé, fág na seanráite mar a bhíodar riamh," a deireann tú. "Tá's aige Dia gur dócha go bhfuil an ceart agat!"

Pat Boran

FOR MY GOLDFISH, VALENTINE

Such enormous sadness
in such a tiny world.
And, looking down at you
in the water clouded
by your flaking scales,
I wonder if my impulse
to take you home
last Valentine's Day
(following a goldfish dream)
was not just a desire
to share my mortal tenancy
of these dusk-facing rooms
under winter's hold.

That dream of gold.
You can imagine how it took me
back into my own smaller body
and bigger, child's imagination
when I found you too
incarnate in a different form.
As the lama recognises
his master in a child,
entering the pet shop,
I knew you then at once—
the golden fish who swam
in the lens of my parents' house,
in the lens of my childhood,
before floating up one day
to leave that world
as I too left that world
as you, too, soon again must leave.

Today in the meantime you look out at me
with the same bewildered eyes you had before,
mouthing the same mute syllable,
the eternal Om that says
nothing changes.

Lead becomes gold and gold lead .
A child will be god when god is dead.

Soon I will recognise your replacement.

John Moriarty

GRAVEYARD ROSE: ROSE WINDOW

There is life and death
And the life of the rose
Is a private post-mortem
Showing its red fingers in Spring.

Under the angel of death
And his star-pronged lance
Headstones twist in a tribal dance
Unknown to hill or hour;
The lightning conductor descends
With bitter power
To set their souls in flight;
Their hands in the earth,
Under earth their eyes,
Touch contradicts the sense of sight.

The heavens tonight
Are on hungerstrike
Over life and death inbreeding;
Only Venus moves
Through the ghost town sky
Of their conceiving;
The void still clings
To the seven days' birth of light,
The wild hare ricochets
Into the hills, all eyes and life,
Its eyes outmanoeuvre it limbs
The kingfisher dives, outmanoeuvering
Night and an image of wings.

Examined by Socratic clay
Our marrow has no answer,
Nor night, nor Judgement Day
Can split its indivisible dust
Or lay the ghosts of fire
And water lust.
The sea encloses many lands
And one, like Yorick's skull
In Hamlet's hands,
Is stripped of all its soil:
Thunder guides the lightning home,
The rose makes public
What was always private in the stone.

Penny Perrick

from **MALINA**

published by Bantam

The architect who designed Malina was English like Harriet and her husband Charles, who is now my husband. It was Charles's idea that the house should rise straight and sheer from the edge of the lake, so that the wooded slope behind it, twittering with birdsong, seemed like a green backdrop to its dove-grey grandeur. Malina exposed its great, grey flanks to the damp, chilly winds which gave it no shelter. A local man would have known better. He would have nestled the house further back into the crook of the woods, made it turn some gentle corners to trick the wind of its prey, created snug, little nooks to sit in and get warm. But Charles and his English architect had no notion that in the west of Ireland a house must offer protection against the rough climate as well as display beauty. They made huge, vaulted rooms with doors of imported mahogany which swelled and then warped in the changeable temperatures, letting cruel draughts nip along the polished floors and chill Harriet's thin limbs that shivered, I was certain, under her heavy skirts. In those high, cold rooms, which only warmed through when the sun smote directly on the vast south-facing windows, even the great fireplaces that the architect had installed looked toy-sized, as though they belonged in a doll's house. Charles Trewin would have nothing of the local marble, a pale, white-veined green stone, splodged with deeper green. He says it reminded him of the soap in his dormitory at Rugby school, a school he loathed. Instead, he ordered snow-white marble from Carrara and brought over English stonemasons to carve rich designs of swags and fruits and angels on the mantelpieces. The fireplaces blazed with turf, popped and crackled with wood from the trees behind the house. Whole tracts of bogland were cut into neat, dark sods to heat that house, scores of young lads spent hours on the bog road, their donkeys, with reed baskets strapped to their sides, quietly waiting until the boys had filled the baskets with turf. And all for the Big House, for Malina, the house that would not grow warm.

I have made Malina seem like an unwelcome and chilly place. In fact, it is magical. Charles Trewin started building it for his bride, Harriet, in 1865, and, by the time I was born, a few years later, in the whitewashed farmhouse on the far side of the lake, that grey enchantment was complete, a fairy palace growing out of the glittering water, its winding drive, plushy with rhododendrons in late spring, leading from tall, wrought-iron gates to the massive, oak front door, sturdy with its stone archway.

Brian Smeaton

GOING WEST TO CLIFDEN

Sunlit flanks of heaving heather
misty hills and smooth water
beyond Croagh Patrick and the sky
is clear and blue
I feel the beauty in my soul
every mile I roll
going west to Clifden

In Ballybofey I picked up
the Spiddal man Brendan O'Tuairisc
going home after a three day
21st party in Letterkenny
and I feel the beauty in my soul
every mile I roll
going west to Clifden

Outside Castlebar Jill Maund
London born living in Westport
for years with children Liam
and Tommo writes poetry
and I feel the beauty in my soul
every mile I roll
going west to Clifden

Westport up the street
and there in one shop window
photographs of Princess Grace
and Prince Rainier from long ago
and I feel the beauty in my soul
every mile I roll
going west to Clifden

Then Sam McAughtry and Tommy Sands
in the Clifden Bay Hotel
singing stories singing songs
full of spirit and clarity
and I feel the beauty in my soul
every mile I roll
going west to Clifden

Pat O' Brien

A BIRTHDAY SONNET
(for A.M.)

There is always a moment when silence,
is our only gift—a time to allow
The earth speak to us, its sudden presence,
Shake us free of self and, again, avow
Our unity with all that lives and seeks
Its freedom. A day, perhaps, when children,
Animals, a crescent beach, far snow peaks
The rivers run demand their own amen.

But mostly we live in wounded places
Where dark thoughts scar and scab the heart and mind
And all we have to touch truth are faces
Whose eyes insist that we be, at least, kind.
Somewhere between life both as gift and pain
We know ourselves, are granted the human.

Peter Fallon

A HUMAN HARVEST

Our wishes quicken into flesh
and yield a human harvest.
Remembered, revived—
the parts of a family
flock home to nest.

His sister, our daughter—
we clutch her as a text
of faith. He needs to know,
Will she still be here in the morning?
Yes, love, tomorrow, and the next.

Rita Ann Higgins

I ASKED HIM ABOUT THE HORSES

'Don't talk to me about horses
they're running backwards
one let me down badly
in a Yankee yesterday,
the gennet'

More lotto talk,
'England have the lotto now,
what they can't steal from us
they copy '

More mano over there talk
more when I get out things will be different talk
back then to safer ground
a hurricane called Gordon is devouring Florida
a place for Irish weather
a place for every horse since Arkle
a race for mints

'Go on, go on I tell you,
take one, one for the bus'.

Ted McNulty

ANOINTED

My father's chair
is vinyl green and
where the big head
touched is oiled
with years of
vaseline jelly he
used on his hair
to save money
for final expenses

Never once did
I rest my head on
that chair until
the night of the
wake and up to me
now to make the
first move I lean
back and I do it
I touch him at last

Lucile Redmond

THE GLORY OF THE REICH

"A BEAUTIFUL skin," he said, drawing it across the table towards him. "Is it human?"

"Subhuman."

"Of course."

He handled the skin. It had been cured; he could work with it. It gave off a dim light in the darkened room, and he could faintly make out a tattoo: Liebchen.

"Yes, I can make your lampshade." He rose and lifted off the blackout curtain, and the flame of the candle disappeared in the light. It was a beautiful day, the rain sweeping perpendicularly into a lashed sea. A figure on the sea road stood like the digit 4, a raised arm holding an umbrella. No gulls were visible, no seals. He turned back to the guard. She had come up silently behind him.

"I have to go now," he said.

She was not looking at the rain falling into the sea, but at the photograph of Lila and Gertrud, propped in the window where he could see them watching him when he looked out to the lighthouse to see whether the moon had passed it.

"I have to go." he said. "An appointment".

He gave the glowing skin a last look and collected the gift-wrapped present he had stored in the corner: a toy train, wooden; too young really -

"I'll go as far as the gate with you," he told the guard.

They walked out together, the big guard and he—she held the door for him, but at the gate she went up towards the hotel and he turned to walk along the seafront, past the train station and the busy loading platform.

The hospital was full of soldiers. Most had not yet been seen to, but they were silent, sitting in their stained bandages as the doctors rushed from one to the next. He stepped between them up the corridor to the children's section. Lila's bed was empty, they had moved her again. He looked in to the sister's cubicle.

"My daughter?"

"Yes, I was wondering. Where did she go?" Suddenly she smiled. He was startled. She had never smiled before. "Oh! She woke up?"

"No—I don't know. I thought you would know. Just—her toys are still there?"

She shook her head. "There's been some big move, I think. Probably to make room for all the soldiers - you saw?" She leaned forward and said softly: "A big battle. Near Paris, they say."

"I'd better speak to the administrator."

But the administrator's office was empty. He left the gift-wrapped train on the desk and went back to the entrance hall. Dr Kant was the most senior there. He stopped her between two soldiers and asked her. "I don't wish to bother you. My daughter."

The doctor put a hand on his arm. "It's for the best."

"What's for the best? Where is my daughter? Where is my little girl?"

The doctor stepped back. "She's been moved to another hospital. More specialised. The administrator can tell you which one."

"But the administrator is not in his office."

"I can't help you, Otto. All the coma patients went different places, the adults to Berlin, I think, the children I don't know."

He looked at the clock. It would wait till later. He would go and pick up the hides from the station, get some work done. The administrator was always at his desk in the afternoon.

There was an interminable wait in the station. They were loading another of the big trains for the work camps, and the hordes milled around, losing their packages, the young SS men occasionally cracking a head to keep order. An unshaven man even snatched at his arm as he passed, trying to say something.

At last he got out and brought his pack of hides back to the apartment. They were heavy so he took a tram. He had not driven since a while after the accident.

He met his downstairs neighbour at the gate. She was excited. Someone was selling paraffin on a stall in the city road.

They ran in for five-gallon tanks and ran with them banging behind them on trolleys. They had to queue for quite a while.

"Did you see the big consignment of Jews?" she muttered to him in the queue. "They're stepping up the programme - filling the labour camps for the war effort."

The queue was full of rumours; there must be a physical system involved where queues fertilise rumours, form the correct growing medium.

In the end she got three gallons and he got two, enough to make life easy for an unimaginable length of time if he used the primus only to bring the stew to the boil and then put it quickly into the haybox each time. He even got some meths.

"How is Lila," she said, "Any change? I find your devotion so admirable."

"Admirable." Lila and Gertrud running forward naked to plunge into the sea on a rainswept night, the moonlight picking out the shadows on mother and daughter's plump forms, the two falling laughing into the waves, turning to laugh back at him as he hopped on one foot untying his shoelaces.

"Admirable?" They walked home together, talking of the old days. He told her about the day Gertrud had jumped into a mountain lake wearing all her clothes because the water looked so beautiful she could not wait to undress.

He turned the key in the lock. "They've moved Lila. Some specialist hospital." When he turned back to her he saw her eyes on him.

As he worked the leather for the guard's lampshade he kept thinking of that day, of Gertrud's eyes, as silver as the Dalmatian dog's, looking up at him out of the silver-grey water until he had plunged in too and they had kissed as they swam, going under, so that the water went up his nose and they came up laughing and raced around and around in circles, swimming with the clean new strokes the Americans had introduced, stretching forward and forward in the ice-cold lake.

The leather worked beautifully—he managed to make the tattoo come up, and found another, a millimetre-sized heart with a butterfly perching on it, it must have been near the neck. He placed it so the light came through it, throwing its shadow on the wall behind when the bulb was lit.

They were going to the sea that day too, the three of them in the English car he had brought back from his hiking holiday in France when he was 18; Lila was eight then, she was in a temper because she could not find her bathing suit, they were going to a beach that was often quite crowded. He had not had the money to get the car checked. Blood and seawater had mixed on the road. "We have been able to save your little girl," the doctor had said. He said nothing about his wife.

He finished the work. It was not the kind of thing he liked, but it was artistically sound: it had merit. And the guard would pay. She had spoken first of some triumphal lettering, but fell silent then, and asked instead for a simpler style.

He left it there and went up again to the hospital, hurrying past the station where they were still loading the long train. Cattle trucks had been shunted on to a siding, and soldiers and civilians were standing in an arguing, queueing mass, waiting for their tickets to go east.

It was mealtime in the hospital. The corridors were full of the smell of cabbage and potato-water. The administrator was not there. Lila's room was occupied by three soldiers, each semi-conscious; one boy's eyes rolled to follow him as he looked for her toys.

He looked again for Dr Kant, and found her sitting at a table in the canteen, a novel propped before her.

"Dr Kant, you must tell me," he said, twisting a thumb in a white-knuckled fist. "Where can I obtain information."

The doctor said: "Otto, take some food. It is good German sausage today." He turned and went out. Outside he wandered back up to the station. He met his neighbour on the way. He heard her calling, running after him—she had been queueing for flour and heard another rumour. The big mental hospital in the next town, she said; all the patients had been evacuated to a labour camp, to make room for more soldiers.

"But some of those patients could not work. I have talked to doctors. Some are catatonic, or violent."

"Those, of course, they must leave," she said. "But it's good, is it not, that many who could never have been thought able to work will return to an active part of the community? Out of war, good can come."

He walked back along the seafront and let himself in: his neighbour did not come with him this time, she had heard of some coal in High Street.

He stood by the cooker, turning the pressure knob back and forward, his eyes on the window and its view of sea, lighthouse, sky. His gaze was drawn to the picture of Gertrud and Lila, cheek pressed to cheek, their smiles bearing the same dimple below the corner of the mouth.

In the distance, muted by the window, sounding faintly under the roar of the waves on shingle, he could hear the train start.

Sheila O'Hagan

SISYPHUS

She pushes up and down the hill from home
to supermarket with the babykart
the bag of wash, the toys for the park.
In a month the new baby will come,
the wash grow bigger, and the little lad
run off up and down the shopping aisles.
She stops to draw a hand across her back,
light up a fag, count out her life in child
allowance days. Tomorrow she will trail
round to the clinic, have her stomach probed,
get weighed, her urine tested, and be told
he should do some voluntary, not be home
so much. She doesn't answer them. Sometimes
she paints her face and goes out with the girls.

Billy Roche

ALLELUIA

I tiptoe into the chapel. The choir is up on the organ loft singing the Alleluia from the mass that I've just written. It will be recorded and a snatch of it used in my stage play The Cavalcaders which opens at The Abbey Theatre in a few nights time. When word gets around that I've arrived the men grow a little restless and the choir master chastises them. "Settle down," he tells them. "Concentrate." And so they take another stab at it and when it's over seventy innocent faces peer down over the bannister to see what I think of it. Some of them call down to me. Was it alright? How does it sound? I tell them it sounded grand. "One more time," the choir master says and off they go again, their voices lilting and a hint of a Wexford accent peeking out through the beautiful curtain of sound that echoes up and down the chapel.

This is the Wexford Male Voice Choir. As a boy I watched these men going off to work in the factories and dusty malt stores. I watched them dodging, dirty faced, home for their dinner every day. These are the insurance men and the milkmen and the bank clerks and the teachers and the postmen who thronged the bars and the snooker halls and the hurling matches. These are the men who walked the greyhounds and climbed up into the pigeon lofts of the town way back in those distant days of dray horses and half doors. And to think now that they are gathered here to sing my song! Needless to say the notion that I may live forever crosses my mind.

I have rambled up the aisle to stand outside the confession box and a slight shiver of deja vu creeps over me. As a scrupulous lad I returned to this place time and time again to tell the priest the same little sins over and over. So much so that in the end the man got fed up of me and told me that he was going to give me what was called a general absolution which would forgive me for everything I ever did, thought or said. It would also forgive me, he said, for everything I ever thought I did, or thought, or said, even... I came out of there walking on air, sailing past the guilty-eyed adulterers and drunkards who were waiting nervously in line.

And then there's the marble altar rails. Inside there I served my first mass. The priest on that wintry morning was an elderly man who for some strange reason insisted that I stand behind him when he was giving out communion instead of in front which was the proper way to do it. I was raging with him. Half the women from John Street had come to see me make my debut as an altar boy. Now they would be thinking that I had got it wrong and I would have to spend the next week explaining to them that it was all the priest's fault. My job was to hold the silver plate under the chins of the communicants just in case the Holy Host should take a tumble. We were always led to believe that if that happened the priest would have to come out after mass and get down on his hands and knees and scrub the spot where it had landed. And give a guess who'd get the blame for it? Yeah, right. Oh the pressure!

One of our first customers that morning was a mute man who had little or no control over his tongue. It darted in and out of his mouth like a snake on the rampage. In and out and up and down. No logic to it at all. It nearly put the heart crossways in me trying to keep track of it. In the end the priest, who could be a fairly contrary individual at the best of times, just gave up the ghost altogether and moved along and left him there Communionless.

It was shortly after that I hitched a lift down to the chapel with the local coalman. I was on my way to serve early morning mass, dawdling through the silent streets. The coalman inveigled me into doing a few errands for him and, to make a long story short, I ended up late for mass. I hurried out onto the altar with dirty hands and a big dirty face. The priest reared up cat melodian on me after mass. The cheek of me to come out onto the altar like that he said. And I was falling behind with my chapel rent. He had a good mind to turf me out of the altar boys altogether he said and if I ever needed a reference then I needn't bother coming to him because he wouldn't give it to me. My eyes glistened with tears as he towered over me. For days after I wondered what this reference was that he wouldn't give me.

This little scene would haunt me for many years—the fact that this ascetic looking saint just couldn't bring himself to find anything funny in a dirty faced little altar boy. Nearly thirty years later the incident would form the basis of a scene in my play Belfry when the young troubled priest rounds viciously on the little simple minded altar boy for some minor misdemeanour.

The choir are beginning to disperse. "It's a wrap," someone says good humoredly. I go and hang out in the porch as the men come one by one down the winding stairs. Like a nervous father of the bride I wait to shake hands with them all and thank them for coming and so on... They drift on out into the dwindling daylight to light up cigarettes and to shoot the breeze and I mingle with them a while, basking in the notion that sometimes small talk can be a wonderful thing.

And then they start to scatter off home in all directions—towards The Faythe and John Street and Bride Street and Salty Avenue. And as the last few stragglers disappear around the bend I turn to discover that I'm stranded on the far side of a river that I never meant to cross. The choir has carried me here it seems; on a transparent bridge that is now evaporating before my eyes. All of a sudden I'm a man! A Father! A husband! I mean what's going on? Everybody knows that this was never supposed to happen to me. I'm a child of the sixties. I was never meant to grow up. NEVER!

The very last member of the choir comes out of the chapel, blessing himself. He smiles at me reassuringly and runs off to catch up with a cluster of men that have gone ahead of him, calling out to them innocently to wait for him. His hair is receding and he is going grey at the temples although I know for a fact that he is younger than me. Suddenly I'm plagued with the thought that I'm probably old enough to run for mayor or something. On top of that a little girl going by calls me mister, if you don't mind. Mister, though!

Now I'm alone in my little Gethsemane with the grey sky above and an Alleluia at my back. There is a small bird balanced on a wire overhead and in the words of John Cooper Clarke, "there's a rainbow in the road," and although I cannot find the right words to express it there is also a strange feeling of forgiveness in the air.

Alle...alle...alleluia.

Greg Delanty

THE GIFT
(to two emigrants, Orlaith & Gerry, who returned to Ireland to be married)

It rained cats & dogs all day on your day:
the day you'll open up in an album
back on Broadway & sentimental eyes will stray
over this snap or that of a sozzled chum
after a stave, bellising his noble call:
aunts connishuring under umbrellas and confetti;
uncles promising to take the tack after it all;
you knowing you're poxed despite the pawny.
laughing at the razzing behind a camera
or slagging characters you've not seen in Yonks
as photos curl in dog days of America
and you curse the sleepless, humid Bronx
wishing for your wedding day gift of rain—
its absence a dry, out-of-the-blue pain.

Desmond Hogan

PATERA

"You'll never fit in here," an Irish woman whom I very vaguely knew told me when I came to live in London permanently. It was on a street in West London, still war-time colours—teal blues, Santa Claus reds—lampposts like liquorice twisters, a pastel billboard for rock fish, scampi, skate, cod roe, savaloy, spam fritters outside Gunn's fish and chip shop, fly-blown glass. 'The West Indians, the Indians fit in here. But the Irish never.' A very fat young man in a black, collared T-shirt, a scarlet line in the collar, stood on the street, an earring in each ear.

Afterwards, about a year later, I had tea in that woman's small and sparse flat. A photograph on the wall of a visit to New York—a girl with sixties bouvant in a blue-grey dress with white constellations on it against cornflower blue skyscrapers. A photograph of girls in emergent strawberry chequered dresses outside a country cottage. A wedding photograph, a woman in a turban hat with wings at the back standing very straight beside the girl with the sixties bouvant who looked more ill at ease than she'd been in New York. White crockery with borders of alternate squares of blue and pink roses in a cabinet.

A black woman in a hip length jacket walks, head in the air, with a bunch of salmon-coloured carnations by the station at Champion Park.

A boy with shorn hair holds the hand of a little girl in a long tartan dress with an Eton collar and button-up patent boots.

On the railway platform a young British Rail worker stands, military shoulders, cropped hair, in mauve-carmine shoes with blond bristles on them, dunes in his face.

A boy darts among the congregation of homeless near Victoria

Station, hands behind his back, red military cap on his head.

"Why are you wearing a beret? Are you in the Foreign Legion?"
"Do you remember Bridget the Midget?" two tramps are in conversation on the ground near me.

A boy who said he was doubly incontinent and that he'd been an alcoholic since he was twenty asks about the trains back to Nottingham.

"Where are you going to sleep tonight?" the boy in the military beret shouts at a woman whose head is annealed by many scarves.

A former tramp called Rose, in a pink taffeta dress, on crutches, has come to visit her former companions. "I live in Kings Cross now. Dreadful place. Six year olds beat up old women."

In an arcade a Liverpool boy sings a song he'd written himself: "I want to go home."

On the journey to Ostend, in a part of the ship deserted but for the two of us, an old Jewish man in a hat and in a prayer shawl, tallow and black striped, leans over a table, quietly droning prayers for those at sea.

In Antwerp Central Station there is a fanfare of yellow embossments on the cafeteria wall. The chandeliers are gold cylinders. Little nuns in oyster grey slouch by and the men's lavatory is filled with mimosa and gypsophilia and women in flowered dresses.

At the cafeteria counter someone in a beige jersey carded with London smells leans towards me as if to say something.

The trimming of the city across the square from the station—lime trees, plane trees, advertisements for McDonalds.

A tramp walks his bicycle with all his belongings on it by the station.

"Most people think we are just dossers. They don't know the background," a tramp had told me outside Victoria Station before I got the train.

A man in a sailor's cap, a black sleeveless jersey, blows a gold horn which had been hanging around his neck, by the river, to announce the departure of a boat. A man with bald head like unopened hawthorn blossom is staring at the river.

In a Jewish cafe near the station I have a coffee and warm almond boluses. On the wall is a black and white photograph of an old Jewish lady giving chrysanthemums to Princess Juliana September 9, 1938 in the Jewish Invalid Hospital.

The streets of Amsterdam are like cobwebs on plantation oaks in the Southern States—the windows and transomes of bars and cafes crowded with things, the packed flotsam of one window connecting with that of another—dolls in flamingo silks, stains on their faces and the same stains running over pigs clasping their breasts: cups in the shape of buxom monks: cowled monks with their hands enveloped in their gowns; the head of Winston Churchill, cheeks very rouged, ruff at his neck; cherubs throwing their legs in the air like can-can dancers: a teddy bear in a cage with monkeys painted on tympanums beneath him: a Dreste's cocoa tin—burnt orange—with a girl in Dutch costume carrying pails on it: a small placard—Je ne fume que le Nils—with a girl in lavender robes and raffia sandals smoking a cigar by the Nile: a pig chanteuse with long gloves, blonde sideswept hair: a bear doctor with a stethoscope; Santa Claus with a hyacinthine beard, little purple bells and acorns in it: two huge swans, one on either side, hem in a table with Turkish weaving on it—purple with yellow, orange and olive flowers: a pyramid of tins of fanta, coke in the window of a Turkish cafe, the ceiling scuffed with little black marks; a display of pear flans, forest berry bavoroises, orange cakes with a litter of little orange fruit on them, mounds of white smoothened icing: piles of Disque Blue cigarettes: heaps of many coloured buttons, some in transparent tubes.

Stone beavers snuggle into seventeenth century dates on the wall; there's a Moor in dog-rose garb. In the windows are camellias, liatris, purple statice; tin pitchers of daisies outside houses.

Years ago I knew a girl from Galway who came here and had a flat near the Casa Rossa nightclub, a shower of fuschine lights on the canal outside at night. I met her in Amsterdam once, in a cafe where a Chinese man was sitting under photographs of Buddhist monasteries, on a day of autumn sunshine. I was with a girl who had lemon yellow hair. The girl from Galway was wearing a blouse with yellow ducks on it. She died in Amsterdam some months after that, of a heroin overdose.

A girl in a leghorn hat with a red cloth rose in it and in a dress of double squares of pale blue on white, red roses at the edges of the squares, cycles by and looks directly into my eyes, first time in months it seems someone looks directly into my eyes.

A woman in a dress of pale yellow in squares of pale blue line, dark blue corners to the squares, stands outside a pigeon shop.

In another square an old Askenazi Jewish man with corkscrew curls smokes a pipe with a fist carved at the end of it. A barge comes through a narrow canal.

Two women in flowered dresses, one of the dresses with a white collar, sit on a wall in a little cul de sac, a Turkish woman in white behind them, a ceramic rooster in a transome.

In the Saint Francis Xavier Church on Singel a woman and little boy light a candle in front of a statue of a gold Virgin with rubric undersleeves and a child with gold bracelet on his wrist and a gold apple in his hand.

Moving always reminds me of one story houses of London brick orange between the South Circular Road and the Grand Canal, with mustard or green doors and flaxen stains on the lace curtains and crockery with Greek key patterns in the windows and a sense of lives within with gashes in them.

My relationship with England once was the harebell-blue of the sea between Calais and Folkestone in November, coming back from days of the Riviera dei Fiori, having lost my passport, being interrogated by police who'd inspect a card from a tiny hotel on the Passeggiata di Via Roma, Alassio or a postcard of an ivory Virgin.

When I first arrived in London in 1970, after getting a room in Kilburn, the first outing I made was to Hampstead Heath. It was July, late afternoon, and the houses on the margin of the Heath were lighted up, wine doors, diamond shapes, and flowers in the lace curtains, lozenge shapes in the transomes, Japanese red maple trees in cobbled front yards, white rose bushes, great terracotta pots placed in bohemian nonchalance.

There'd been an Italian man in a zouave cap hanging like a plum to one side with a dancing bear in a fair on the Heath.

In the following few weeks I saw sunflowers, lobelias, chrysanthemums, geraniums, candytuft, autumn narcissi, saffron, lavender, poppies, jasmine come to those gardens.

I sat on benches with many arms, fretwork of Nile green and turquoise, with single nettles or fool's parsley coming through them as though waiting for a partner.

The names on the War Memorial at the top of the Heath, against the autumn sunsets, were Gildersleeves, Cloutman, Wolfred, Budd, Plaistowe, Selbie, Dawbarn, Younge, Sandalay, Schleichert, Howlett.

In the town I came from, which I'd left a year before to go the

University in Dublin, there'd been a little Royal British Legion hut, under chestnut trees, when I was a child, with war memorials

inside to those killed in Ypres and Givency, names like Munnelly, Sharkey, McGillicuddy, Sheehy.

For one year I took a room in a house by the Heath but something happened, a fractional, divisive incident, and I left.

But the Heath remained my Etruscan patera—the saucer representing eternal continuity in the hands of effigies on Etruscan sarcophagi—and this spring, knowing I had to move again, I frequented it more than ever.

Looked at the white hawthorn, red and mauve on the petals with a custard pungency inside. The sweet violets with forks of deeper colour coming out of a dawn-like evanescence in the centre. Bluebells with stripes inside like those on awnings or on Sienese heraldry, insects running inside them. Near the War Memorial a bed of purple pansies with deep yellow spots on one side of the centre and pale yellow crescents on the other.

Became acquainted with the crested grove on one of the ponds, fork of is head, amber at the back of his head, ruff at the neck.

Since March swam out to the coots' nest in a lifebuoy on the Men's Pond where the young were hatching.

Two swans came to live on the Men's Pond.

Perhaps because it was coming towards the D-Day anniversary, my landlady for twelve years, pepper-salt hair, in a pinafore with hankie in the breast pocket, borders to the pinafore, under a photograph of Prince Albert and Princess Elizabeth, took out family photographs. She was the only girl in a South London family of boys.

The older boys, crinkled hair—marcel waves—of the thirties. "Friday night is the Amani night," we used to say, stressing the exaltation of shampoo. A tie with stripes going horizontally on the knot and vertically otherwise. White shirts with sleeves in twisted rolls.

Four of the brothers were killed in the war.

She served in the Women's Royal Navy Service in Trincomalee in North East Ceylon.

But she was in South London for V-Day celebrations. Long tables in the open air, benches; Union Jacks hanging from windows, paper chains between houses, cut out' paper bells above the tables, flowers in jugs, incongruously some of the women in cloche hats and some of the little girls in winter caps, a boy staring at the camera—displaying his legs in long, dark stockings with lines of jonquil brightness in them, my landlady also staring at the camera, in a leopard skin coat with epaulettes and black sleeves.

A trip with a surviving brother in the nineteen fifties from Victoria to Seattle, on a ship under Golden Lion Bridge, the man's hair seduced in Eastman colour to henna, the flag of Canada with its cherry maple leaf blowing.

By the sea with the same brother, his hair crescendo curled from the right side, in spectator shoes, black and white, with two bars of black going through the white in the middle, advertisements for Wills' Capstan and Walls' Icecream and Brookebond tea.

Later that day I passed a black wedding party in a front garden in Lewisham Way, a black woman in an apricot dress, black net over her face, looking towards the bus, another woman with a string of petals in her hair, another with silver pea-pods in her hair.

Although it was the beginning of summer I thought of South East London at the end of summer, black mustard growing in waste under huge graffiti 'Maggie's Dream', black girls pushing British Rail trolleys through the grass.

Today I find no clue, no lead on a room in Amsterdam and I go into a cafe with brown armchairs with very low seats and lamps with brown lampshades, the kind the girl I came to Amsterdam with years ago and I would have gone to.

Lamplight partly lights up a Rembrandt poster on the wall, a

Jewish wedding, the ring on the first finger of the girl's right hand showing it's a Jewish wedding.

I see my face in a mirror, grey at the edges of my hair the way there's brown on the edges of the camellia flower.

The face of the girl from Galway I knew years ago come back too, Jewish peoths, inspired by Amsterdam, on either side of her face. Recently in London I met a boyfriend of hers from Galway, who's had a lot of breakdowns—once very beautiful, now his curly hair gone grey but his face still young and rosy like pinks in a country-woman's lapel. He's taking a course in the University of London. And he says he's happy.

Outside again, in the late afternoon sunshine, a wedding party goes by on a barge, old ladies in crinoline seated in a line, young men standing, singing 'Champagna. Champagna'.

I take the train the Zandfoort aan Zee, passing a blue circus tent with auric stars on it.
'Nec mihi Dulichium domus est Ithaceve Samosve... My home is not Dulichium or Ithaca or Samos.'

The windows of Zandfoort ann Zee are crowded with sea things— swans with shells at their rear, ships with sails of shells, a Chinese boy in a romper suit, a pear of hair on his bald head, sitting on an amber fish, holding up a lamp: an old Chinese woman kisses the nude breast of a young Chinese woman in the middle of this jumble, a ceramic cat peeps out of a ceramic giftbox, there's a flowering cactus in a pig. Inside one window I see a table, a small bible at each place.

On the beach are shells—saffron and white, white with indigo lines, pure white.

A man in a rose-scarlet shirt goes by in a trotter drawn by a horse, just alongside the waves.

I am in another place, Iowa, an Amish couple in a buggy against the September corn, the man in a pork pie hat, the woman in a poke bonnet.

An old man, just back from Eastern Europe, on a boat on the Mississipi, head in hands, the wispish hair which covered his head albino-white, the American flag blowing, yellow leaves on the boat.

A group photograph by a picture window against the corn fields. A Chinese woman in a melon stole with tassels, big loops of glasses, bent over laughing, a taciturn boy with guinea gold hair beside her.

The gargantuan apartment block in which I stayed by the corn, dozens and dozens of apartments which looked uniform outside but inside had cabinets of crockery with papaya roses inside. We used to have feasts and conversations there.

London, South East London, where I moved after Iowa has always been lonely for me. Loneliness needs to be dissolved in me, my life needs to be soldered again with a community.

There was six months in Berlin, a feast in May with a German boy who frequently visited me in South East London and who was to die a little over a month later of Aids—gingerbread, dessert apricots, biscuits from a tin with a goldfish bowl on it—the buildings of Kreuzberg amber in the sunset.

A few months before he died he went to Amsterdam and bought a shirt which had patterns based on a scarf in a William van Vlite painting, red maple leaves.

"And it came to pass, when he made an end to speaking unto Saul, that the soul of Jonathan was knit with the soul of David, and Jonathan loved him as his own soul,"

The old man on the boat was to see me during a trip to Berlin but he died at O'Hare Airport in Chicago.

"...Then a boat up the Rhine Bonn-Mainz, where my one remaining German relative will meet us and for five days we will drive around the Black Forest and visit the small town from which my ancestors emigrated to America."

It was as if Iowa and Berlin were gilded into one another like parts of a mirror in a Victorian pub, a mirror with a cornucopia back-painted onto it or maybe pomegranates. But this mirror—mirrors—reflected the cornfields of Iowa in November and the lime trees of Berlin in May.

In the mirror too is the face of the boy who died of Aids. Just before he died he looked more composed than ever, pink-ochre, circle necked jersey, black nylon hair. "It's the inner freedom. Lose that and you're dead anyway."

South East London; Victorian chimneys: a brioche called Sallyslung in the small windows of old bakeries: a piebald horse, brown and white, drawing a cart with old fridges on it: old women with globe-like hair-dos and tottering steps on long roads with one magnolia tree: where men's tattoos were often the ensignia of jails—a chain going down an arm to the wrist, huge keys, firmly barred windows: Irish tramps with psoriasis on their feet; South East London the place of the shibboleth—a sudden spit on the pavement.

But the loneliness, the lack of contact with community.

I must move on now from loneliness and give them back their community intact, without me.

"But when they persecute you in this city, flee ye into another."

When I first came to live in South East London people I'd met in Iowa or as part of my journey to Iowa would come to visit me, sit by the fire, bring stories of their countries and their cities.

An English boy with a sleeper in his ear, dimple on his chin, who'd worked in community centres for Catholic and Protestant children in Belfast, with whom I'd platonically shared a bed in New York, came with his Jewish fiancee, who brought sugar pretzels. My can Eamon was a tiny kitten then.

That was January.

I'd gone to a party in London that Christmas with my friend from Germany, in a cardigan that was the colour of the night sea off Palestine.

The previous September, before I'd moved in here, just after the Sabra and Chatila massacres, I'd been to Israel, resolved myself in the electric blue September light, saw a group of girls on horses go by on the sands, under palm trees, at the Mediterranean near Tel Aviv.

When I returned from Israel and moved into the little flat there was at first a sense of the cornfields of Iowa merging into the place, the way mirrors in a Victorian pub overlap, are gilded onto one another. Then the visitors stopped coming.

A woman from Ireland, chestnut haired, exiled in London, came in a hobble skirt and in a wide brimmed hat with chick feathers on it my first Christmas here and called the food 'beauteous'. That was the night my young friend arrived from Germany. He returned again and again, replacing the people I'd met in Iowa.

And I, as though by covenant, managed to be close to him when he was dying his young and very painful death.

Alone against the Mediterranean I am again—the walled city of Acca, a tight fistful of stars over the sea, areca palms near the port, voices in the dark streets,—fighting Ireland—family, fighting England—incipient denigration. Fighting for survival of 'the inner freedom', fighting to exist.

The sunset is gone now and the man in the trotter and Iowa and Israel. The journey is a dead-end. There is no country. My only country is the flag of postcards on the wall—wherever that may happen to be.

But the patera, the continuity goes on, Hampstead Heath, Zandfoort aan Zee, the cornfields of Iowa: a walk into a November sunset with the American flag and a flag with the wild rose of Iowa blowing over pumpkins and a look back onto a house, where someone has just sung 'My Tennessee Mountain Home', flaring like someone pulling a cigarette in the night—one of life's few houses of friendship.

Christy Kenneally

FROM THE SCHOOL WINDOW.
CLIFDEN, CONNEMARA.

Slate-grey the lake
beneath a sullen sky.
Yet, here
two opal swans
majestic ply.
And out beyond
behind a veil of grey,
the mountain breasts
the breakers of the day.
And West, far West,
beyond the thrall of night,
ajar the door of heaven,
Ah, the light!

Robert Bly

THE GIANT WHO KNEW ARISTOTLE

Childhood is like a kitchen. It is dangerous
To the mice, but the husband gets fed; he's
An old giant, grumbling and smelling children.
It's a place where you get smaller and smaller.

Or maybe you change size everyday. In general
You become preoccupied with this old lady
In the kitchen.... She putters about, opens oven doors.
The thing is the old woman won't discuss anything.

The giant will. He's always been a fan of Aristotle,
Knew him at school. It is no surprise to him
That the Trojan War lasted ten years, or how it
Ended. He knows something you don't.

Your brother says, "Say, what's that in the oven?"

Sydney Bernard Smith

INISHBOFIN

In the dry stone wall even the odd stone will clunk into a
place, no wobble... a rough intricate fellowship grows
with no wrong shapes, one spot anyway for each...

*

Welly boots shuffle through the blackwrack. The currach
lurches, a maimed insect in the glare, noses into place,
brace the forelegs, sits down by the stern, studiously pre-
pares to disassemble. Like you'd break crabclaws off.

*

...Live by the grave rule of rock and sea, splitting settle-
ments, settling nothing.

*

Love was this summer's answer, rosy clouds passing over
these last years of resistance from Glasillaun Dún, a hundred and eighty feet below where we sat waiting for the
cliff to give way...

*

Toddler and me huddle under a wall while the shower
passes. As if on a metal tray the light slides away up
south, among the skyscrapers and sidestreets of rain that
wander along the Atlantic.

The spade carved a lugworm, it lay in a slowswitch on the palate of reeking mud, festering in the hot forenoon. *O Lord! I am a man and no worm!*

*

Every tillable rood bears the track of the spade. Even in the corners of high places.
'In them days the island was fair hoppin' with people.'
Stone clumps in bracken, at the top of Mikey's field, in childish disarray—rough graves for the children of famine and cholera... The lark looks for an opening in the wind overhead, squirts through her arrangement of their requiem.

*

Under the washing in the kitchen garden, at some inches in earth, seaweed has rotted for our crops. Half a mile west, in five fathom on sand, the longline, the spillet works.
Pull in the line at evening, & the plaice flap like washing.

*

And cottage ruins, nibbled grass wall to wall
& over the doorless threshold
through vacant rafters the south wind
chases a tuft
    ...outside, the ribs
& last planks of a rowboat

struggle under a scutch-grass cargo
...& relics of pipes reddened in the
lee of the gable & talk in the night,
high-pitched gale-engulfed laughter.

Micheal O' Siadhail

TIGHT-WIRE

Strolling fields behind the tent I glance
Figures leaving glares of light.
Wild applause inside.
Elephants to dance;
Now the acrobats delight
Children, now the juggling clown.
someone hand a faded dressing gown.
Steadied, out she'll stride

Over guy-wires, over littered mud and cans
Past an empty pony stall
Slipping in among
Hung-out clothes and vans.
There she'll seem too small and frail.
No one saw who stepped the wire,
Those who clap her clap their own desire.
Someone always young

Slinging ropes between two garden sheds
Full of reckless festive grace
Seems to dare to flout
Endless overheads
Nothing underwrites but space.
Thrills of business just for fun
Touch the dreams of things we might have done.
Steadied, she'll step out.

Maeve Binchy

A CHRISTMAS STORY

When I was young and spoiled and indulged, instead of being old and spoiled and indulged, I decided late one Christmas Eve that I was going to cancel all previous letter to Santa Claus and ask him for a doll's house.

Laboriously and apologetically I wrote all this to Himself and put it up the chimney and retired happily, leaving confusion and sadness amongst those who had bought me a lovely blackboard and 50 pieces of chalk.

A child's Christmas couldn't be ruined, they told each other, but on the other hand all the shops were closed and and doll's house were out. So they tried to make one. For hours and hours, I believe, they laboured on a big box and painted it white and drew windows in it and stuck on chimneys that kept falling off. One of the few rows of their married life developed over the inability to construct a simple thing like a dolls house.
"Boys should have learned carpentry at school," said my mother in despair as the front of the house caved in yet again.

"Women should know about toys," countered my father as he got out the glue pot once more.

Then they thought about straw and making a doll's house, Hawaian style, but this might not be a good idea in case I hadn't heard of Polynesian houses.

"With all the money we pay at that expensive school, they should have taught her that," said my father. But the straw was damp anyway, so that was abandoned.

A doll's igloo with cotton wool as snow was considered and abandoned. A doll's tepee seemed a good idea if they could paint a doll up as an Indian to go with it. But it required bark, skins, or canvas, and so they had to give that up, too, since they had been thinking of making it with a sheet.

They ruminated wistfully about my younger sister then, and now, easier to please in life, who would be delighted with a rattle or a teddy bear or even nothing at all.

"To be fair," said my father,"she is only two. Maeve *is* six."

"I wonder is it normal for a six-year-old to want a doll's house anyway," said my mother. So they had another hour looking up Normal-Six-Year-Olds in Dr Spock or its equivalent, decided it was boringly normal and inconvenient, and went back to work.

They got bricks and stones in from the garden. They looked up a book called *One Thousand Things A Boy Can Do,* but none of them included making a doll's house. My father became interested in one of the things a boy could do which was digging a tunnel in the garden to irrigate the flower beds.

"That's all we need on Christmas Day," said my mother wearily,"for the neighbours to see you irrigating the flowerbeds with tunnels."

***

It was nearly dawn. The fat cherub was asleep with no idea of anything being amiss. They came into my room, set up the blackboard, and wrote a note on it with one of the pieces of chalk!

'Dear Maeve, your chimney is too narrow and I can't get the doll's house down it. Please do not be upset. It will arrive as an extra gift sometime in January. You have been a good girl. All the reindeer are asking for you. Love from Santa Claus.—

It was morning, and with shining eyes I was beaten on them, begging them to wake up. After only two hours' sleep this wasn't easy for them to do. They showed great alarm. Was I going to threaten to leave home! Were there tears and tantrums which would spoil the day for everyone! Not at all.

"You'll never believe it," I said. "Santa Claus wrote me a note. In his own writing. It's on an old blackboard or something, but it's obviously very valuable. Nobody has seen Santa Claus's writing before. We'll have to show it to everyone. We might lend it to a museum."

It was a good Christmas, like all our Christmases were together; the only thing that makes me sad at this time of year is that I may have forgotten to tell them that... but perhaps they knew.

John Montague

HERBERT STREET REVISITED
for Madeleine

I

A light is burning late
in this Georgian Dublin street:
someone is leading our old lives !

And our black cat scampers again
through the wet grass of the convent garden
upon his masculine errands.

The pubs shut: a released bull,
Behan shoulders up the street,
topples into our basement, roaring 'John!'

A pony and donkey cropped flank
by flank under the trees opposite;
short neck up, long neck down,

as Nurse Mullen knelt by her bedside
to pray for her lost Mayo hills,
the bruised bodies of Easter Volunteers.

Animals, neighbours, treading the pattern
of one time and place into history,
like our early marriage, while

tall windows looked down upon us
from walls flushed light pink or salmon
watching and enduring succession.

II

As I leave, you whisper,
'don't betray our truth'
and like a ghost dancer,
invoking a lost tribal strength
I halt in tree-fed darkness

to summon back our past,
and celebrate a love that eased
so kindly, the dying bone,
enabling the spirit to sing
of old happiness, when alone.

III

So put the leaves back on the tree,
put the tree back in the ground,
let Brendan trundle his corpse down
the street singing, like Molly Malone.

Let the black cat, tiny emissary
of our happiness, streak again
through the darkness, to fall soft
clawed into a landlord's dustbin.

Let Nurse Mullen take the last
train to Westport, and die upright
in her chair, facing a window
warm with the blue slopes of Nephin.

And let the pony and donkey come—
look, someone has left the gate open—
like hobbyhorses linked in
the slow motion of a dream

parading side by side, down
the length of Herbert Street,
rising and falling, lifting
their hooves through the moonlight.

Declan Lucey

THE SEARCH

I was told
"Shut up!
Get out and play."

I made friends with
mud and marbles,
kicking stones with
hands in pockets.
Screaming out in anger.

Lonely.
Oh so lonely.
I didn't know
it was then
the search began
to find
the person
I have still
to locate.

Fintan O'Toole

FORKED TONGUES
—The Language of Contemporary Politics

You know the politicians are in trouble when they reach for the Collected Works of William Shakespeare. Charles Haughey, in his final speech to the Dáil in February, 1992, the speech of a defeated and broken man, cast himself as Othello who had "done the State some service and they know't/ No more of that—" The rhetoric of a great dramatist lent an air of nobility to an occasion that might otherwise have seemed like the sad, whimpering end to an unfulfilled career. Even in the 1990s, big words can still dignify small tragedies.

In his speech to the 1993 Sinn Féin Ard Fheis, Gerry Adams, preparing the way, as we now know, for the end of another era, quoted what he called 'the original grey man in a grey suit', Brutus from *Julius Caesar*. He urged John Major to listen to the latter's warning that

> On such a full sea we are now afloat
> And we must take the current when it serves,
> Or lose our ventures.

What is interesting in such quotations is what is left out. In this case, what immediately precedes this quotation is Brutus's realisation that "we, at the height, are ready to decline." What he's saying is not that the tide is with him, but that if he doesn't take the chance while it's going, he's doomed—a much more interesting reflection on Mr Adams's situation.

Even more interestingly, this speech is followed within a minute by the appearance of Caesar's bloody ghost come to haunt Brutus for his violent misdeeds. In context, the quotation is much more poignant than it may have sounded to the party faithful.

Irish politicians, however, have no monopoly of selective use of Shakespeare. A month before Mr Adams's speech, the darling of the right-wing of the Tory party in Britain, Michael Portillo, in a speech to the Conservative Way Forward annual dinner that was widely seen as his bid for leadership of the Thatcherite faithful, made extensive use of Ulysses' speech from Shakespeare's Troilus and Cressida. In it, according to Portillo, "Ulysses explains how order in society depends upon a series of relationships of respect and duty from top to bottom."

He quoted a large chunk of the speech in which Ulysses explains that "when degree is shaked . . . the enterprise is sick." This, in Portillo's speech, gave sanction to his view that Britain had been undermined by the "cynicism of a self-proclaimed elite" of whinging liberals, whose carping was "tearing down the very pillars" of society. Interestingly, Portillo, too, stopped short, in this case of the most famous bit of the speech, in which Ulysses gets to the point—a savage criticism of the abuse of power by greedy rulers:

> Then everything includes itself in power,
> Power into will, will into appetite;
> And appetite, an universal wolf,
> So doubly seconded with will and power
> Must make perforce an universal prey,
> And last eat up himself.

The point of the speech is not that whinging critics should shut up about the Government, but that the rapacity of powerful rulers destroys society, and eventually, the rulers themselves.

It is in fact particularly ironic that Portillo should have chosen *Troilus and Cressida* to support his call for more deference in society. Of all Shakespeare's plays it is the most scurrilously disrespectful. Princes, heroes, rulers and generals—ostensibly of Greece and Troy—are shown to be spoiled, selfish, incompetent and unable to control their lusts. In the context, Mr Portillo might have been wiser not to raise the subject.

What do these pilferings from Shakespeare tell us about political language today? In the first place they tell us that politicians of all varieties, even in the age of the sound-bite, still feel the need for a heightened rhetoric at moments of great significance. Somehow, the intelligent ones instinctively understand the poverty of the language they use in everyday politics, and yearn for a richer tongue in which to signify their own importance. In the second place, though, they tell us that even when borrowing great language politicians can still use it to evade the truth. Between that yearning and that cynicism lies something of the truth of political language now.

Broadly speaking three important things have happened to the language of politics in recent decades. One is that political language has become primarily visual and only secondarily verbal. Television has replaced the public meeting and the parliamentary debate as the crucible of politics, and television is first and foremost a medium for the eyes rather than the ears. How you look when you're speaking (sincere or insincere?); what the background behind you is like (cold or seductive?); how you are dressed (oddly or with a veneer of authority?)—these visual gestures underpin and override the value of what you say on television. The sound-bite—the crisp, memorable phrase—is the politician's acknowledgement that it is more important to be seen than to be heard.

The American theorist Neil Postman captured this phenomenon very well when he wrote of then-President Ronald Reagan:

> Political campaigns are now conducted largely in the form of television commercials. Candidates forego precision, complexity, substance—in some cases language itself—for the arts of show business: music, imagery, celebrities, theatrics.... It is significant, I think, that although our current President, a former Hollywood actor, rarely speaks accurately and never precisely, he is known as the Great Communicator; his telegenic charm appears to be his major asset, and that seems to be quite good enough in an entertainment-orientated politics.'[1]

More profoundly, television has accelerated the collapse of the public realm and contributed to the development of that most dangerous paradox—privatised politics. The very ornateness of classical political rhetoric—the kind you find in Burke or Sheridan, in Lincoln or in Larkin—was a way of drawing attention to the difference between the speaker and the spoken. A speech was not a revelation of the inner personality of the speaker, it was a public and in a sense impersonal intervention. In the television age, though, there is no such thing as impersonal speech. What matters is not whether the speech is true or false but whether it appears sincere.

Another way of putting this is to note, as the American thinker Richard Sennett has done, the reversal of the meaning of the word 'charisma'. In its original, Catholic, sense, charisma separated the priest from the word of God. The power of the ceremony lay outside the character of the priest. In a secular political context, though, 'charisma' carries an opposite charge.

As Sennett puts it:

> In secular society, when 'charisma' is applied to a forceful leader, the origin of his power is more mystifying than in sacred society. What makes a forceful personality forceful? The culture of personality of the last century answered this question by focusing on what the person felt, rather than on what he did. Motives can be good or bad, of course, but in the last century people stopped judging them in this way. The sheer revelation of someone's inner impulses became exciting; if a person could reveal himself in public and yet control the process of self-disclosure, he was exciting. You felt he was powerful, but couldn't explain why. This is secular charisma: a psychic striptease. The fact of revelation arouses: nothing clear or concrete is revealed. Those who fall under the spell of a forceful personality become themselves passive, forgetting their own needs as they are moved. The charismatic leader thus came to control his audience more fully and more mystifyingly than in the older, civilised magic of the Church.[2]

The second thing that has happened is that 'rhetoric' has become a dirty word. In the eighteenth century, when modern democratic politics was in its infancy, such a development would have been unthinkable. Looking back to the Greeks and Romans, theorists of language like the Irishman Thomas Sheridan took it for granted that there was a natural connection between political rhetoric and public virtue:

> Their end was liberty; liberty could not subsist without virtue, nor be maintained without wisdom and knowledge; and wisdom and knowledge, unless communicated with force and perspicuity, were useless to the state.... [3]

Although there is a tendency to associate rhetoric with the era before democratic politics, the era when political speech was the property of a ruling class steeped in classical literature, it is worth remembering that socialism, too, had its great rhetoricians. On the streets of Dublin and Belfast, James Larkin electrified the working-class by forging a language that was both powerfully rhetorical and insistently democratic. Larkin used a religious language to forge an image of the political leader as both priest and congregation, a speaker more articulate than the rest, but one whose very articulacy was a compliment to his audience. He did not flatter his audience as a modern politician would. Daniel Corkery noted of him that "I never heard him speak to the class for which he stood that he did not half offend them by dwelling on the failings which kept them powerless and timid." Yet he used his rhetoric to make his power an image of the potential power of his listeners:

> Don't bother about cheering Larkin—he is but one of yourselves. It is you that want the cheers, and it is you that deserve them. It is you and the class from which I come—the down-trodden class—that should get the cheers and all the good things that follow the cheers. I don't recognise myself—a mean soul like myself in amean body—as being the movement. You are the movement, and for the time being I have been elected as your spokesman.[4]

This assumption that political liberty rested on the quality of rhetoric was destroyed by two things. One was the evidence from the rise of fascism in the 1930s that powerful rhetoric could destroy liberty as well as defend it. The other was the slow but inexorable infiltration of economics and its jargon into political language. Political culture began to award higher marks for the ability to use economic jargon with apparent confidence than for the ability to articulate hopes, needs and fears. At its most extreme, of course, pseudo-scientific language—'collateral damage', 'terminate with extreme prejudice'—has even been used to obscure atrocity.

The third big shift has been the decline of ideologies. In western Europe at least, it has become increasingly difficult for politicians to draw on a resonant hinterland of images and ideas that can be taken to be shared by at least a large part of their potential audience. A genuinely good political orator in the old tradition like Neil Kinnock failed as a political leader because the language he was able to mobilise simply did not have the capacity to move a wide audience any more.

In Ireland, it is patently obvious that most of the sources of accepted political rhetoric have dried up. Catholicism, the Irish language and, above all, the standard language of nationalism and anti-partitionism may still have resonance for some sectors of the electorate. But the problem they represent from a political point of view is that what appeals to one section of the populace almost certainly disgusts another. As Irish society has become more openly divided, politicians have faced the problem that any issue which stirs deep enough emotions in the electorate to be fashioned into usable rhetoric is also bound to be deeply divisive.

Not, of course, that the old language was ever unproblematic. Its difficulties began, perhaps, with de Valera and the signing of the oath, with words as 'an empty political formula . . . an empty formality'. Certainly it continued with all that de facto and de jure stuff in which reality is recognised as only conditionally real, real on sufferance. Words already begin to take on a life of their own, already start to be spoken in ready-made quotation marks.

But that balancing act began to teeter in the last decade. The destruction of Brian Lenihan was the most obvious and dramatic example. In his *Ireland 1912-1985,* Professor Joe Lee describes Brian Lenihan as 'an amicable virtuoso of shadow language', and there were ample opportunities for the display of virtuosity. In the shadow language, words mean what the speaker wants them to mean and, as in Lewis Carroll, whatever I tell you three times is true. But the inescapable realities of Northern Ireland gradually intruded, making the trick impossible.

Who could forget Brian Lenihan's claim, after Mr. Haughey's 'totality of relationships' meeting with Mrs. Thatcher, that 'institutional structures' were the same as constitutional structures, that everything was on the table, that we were within a few years of achieving something which would satisfy our aspirations towards a united Ireland? Who can forget the fun we all had some time later with the insistence of Messrs Haughey and Lenihan that their statement that constitutional change in Northern Ireland would 'come about only' by the consent of the majority was radically different from Garret FitzGerald's statement that constitutional change in Northern Ireland would 'require' the consent of the majority? It made sense that Brian Lenihan's implosion in the 1990 Presidential election campaign was linguistic. As in some weird Kafkaesque parable, language itself, in the form of Lenihan's words on a tape, ambushed its one-time master.

Charles Haughey retreated into mystical rhetoric. By attaching yourself to a beautiful abstraction like the Nation, you can be on everybody's side, the rich and the poor, the farmer and the urban worker, and whatever you're having yourself. In his now famous 1981 ard-fheis address, Mr Haughey told the faithful in strikingly religious terms, that they got the support of the people because Fianna Fail

> represents not this pressure group or that sectional interest this class or that creed, but because in the broad sweep of its membership and their faith and devotion to their own country, there resides what one can well call the 'spirit of the nation'.

The Spirit of the Nation does not need to argue or explain. The party does not justify itself to the people, is not accountable, because it is the people, or at least the people who matter, the real Irish people. "This ard-fheis", Mr Haughey told his congregation in 1984, "speaks with the authentic voice of Irish Ireland". And for a long time, this authentic voice of Irish Ireland could be merged with P. J. Mara's Una Voce, Uno Duce. As Ray Burke declared in 1982 during one of the heaves against Haughey: 'Loyalty to Fianna Fail is loyalty to the nation itself and its social and economic progress.' And since loyalty to the party was loyalty to its leader, then disloyalty to the person of Charles Haughey was an act of treason against the nation.

In replacing Haughey with Albert Reynolds, Fianna Fail thought it would get realism without rhetoric. It believed that Reynolds's 'pragmatism' would work where Haughey's rhetoric had failed. It forgot that in politics, 'pragmatism' was made possible by the cultural, and rhetorical soup in which it swam. It forgot that pragmatism without a rich ideological dressing soon comes to taste like ruthlessness in the mouths of the electorate. Reynolds thought that a culture of clichés—'the buck stops here', 'my door is always open' (and presumably my path is free to walk), 'I'm a straightforward guy and I tell it like it is'—could replace the careful rhetorical construct which was the house that Charlie built. He thought that a few country 'n' western standards could do for him what Yeats and Malraux and Shakespeare had done for Haughey. He thought that the way you influence the climate of opinion is to send writs to newspapers and veiled threats to RTE.

He was wrong, of course. Pragmatism without ideological artifice comes across as ruthlessness. And a politician with too little rhetoric is ultimately no better off than a politician with too much. Albert Reynolds, under the pressure of an election campaign began to speak in tongues. He promised to 'dehumanise the social welfare system'. He attacked the Fine Gael Leader, 'John Unionist'. He dismissed his opponents' views as 'crap, pure crap'. In leading Fianna Fail to its worst election result since the 1930s, he discovered that the alternative to rhetoric is not pragmatism. It is gibberish.

Politics is thus in the uncomfortable position of being vaguely aware of the need for a rhetoric, but utterly uncertain as to where to look for it. Thus the dominance of speechwriters, spin-doctors, and press handlers. The centrality of the speechwriter has created a kind of pseudo-rhetoric which has all the cadences of the old language but none of its intent. The intention is no longer to communicate clearly but to produce the illusion of communication. It is not to arouse the audience but to keep it happy. For the speechwriter writes not what he or she thinks (by definition what the speechwriter thinks is irrelevant) but what he or she thinks the audience wants to hear. In the era of polling, the purpose of a political speech is not to communicate with the public but to speak in the public's own voice. The pollsters find out what the majority wants to be told. The speechwriter shapes it to the politician's own agenda. The politician delivers the speech. The flaw, of course, is that the majority may not know quite what it wants to hear.

The result is the most effective political speech is also the most meaningless. George Bush, for instance, came from fourteen points behind in the 1988 presidential election in the United States on the basis of three phrases which were put in his mouth by his Irish-American speechwriter Peggy Noonan: "I want a kinder gentler nation" . . . "Read my lips, no new taxes" . . . and "This is America—a brilliant diversity spread like stars, like a thousand points of light in a broad and peaceful sky." Only one of these phrases—the one about taxes—actually had a concrete content, and that content was a flat contradiction of the other two. No new taxes meant a nastier, rougher America, one less able to protect its diversity by cherishing its ethnic poor. But the rhetoric itself, based on polls showing what the electorate wanted, worked by successfully obscuring its own meaning, by giving the illusion of content without the need for thought.

The signs are, however, that democratic electorates throughout the world are becoming less and less susceptible to the pseudo-rhetoric of spin-doctors. The attempts by the New Right in the 1980s to annex some of the key words of society— 'liberty', 'family', 'community'— to narrow and cynical meanings has failed. So has the attempt by the same New Right to promote the language of the marketplace over the language of democracy—substituting 'client' for 'citizen', 'market' for 'country' and 'efficient' for 'just'. But no one has yet managed to construct a syntax in which those keywords, and others like 'equality', 'solidarity' and 'society', become again capable of bearing real meaning. Whoever manages to refurbish a genuine political language for the 21st century may also control politics. That is a source both of fear and of hope.

1   *Conscientious Objections. London, 1988, pp. 169-70*

2   *The Fall Of The Public Man. Faber & Faber, London, 1993, pp. 269-70*

3   *Thomas Sheridan, British Education: Or the Source of the Disorders of Great Britain. London, 1756, pp. 47-48.*

4   *Quoted in James Larkin, by Emmet Larken, London, 1968, p. 145.*

Michael Gorman

THE PEOPLE I GREW UP WITH WERE AFRAID

The people I grew up with were afraid.
They were alone too long in waiting-rooms,
In dispensaries and in offices whose functions
They did not understand.

To buck themselves up, they thought
of lost causes, of 'Nature-boy'
O'Dea who tried to fly
From his bedroom window,
Of the hunch-backed, little typist
Who went roller-skating at Strandhill.
Or, they re-lived the last afternoon
Of Benny Kirwan, pale, bald,
Protestant shop-assistant in Lydon's drapery.
One Wednesday, the town's half-day,
He hanged himself from a tree
On the shore at Lough Gill.

And what were they afraid of? Rent
collectors, rate collectors, insurance men.
Things to do with money. But,
Especially of their vengeful God.
On her death-bed, Ena Phelan prayed
That her son would cut his hair.

Sometimes, they return to me.
Summer lunchtimes, colcannon
For the boys, back-doors
Of all the houses open, the

News blaring on the radios.
Our mother's factory pay-packet
Is sitting in the kitchen press
And our father, without
Humour or relief, is
Waiting for the sky to fall.

John O'Donohue

CONAMARA IN OUR MIND

It gave us
the hungry landscapes,
resting upon
the unalleviated
bog-dream,

put us out
there, where
tenderness never settled,
except for the odd nest
of grouse mutterings
in the grieving rushes,

washed our eyes
in the glories of light.

In an instant
the whole place flares
in a glaze of pools,
as if a kind sun
let a red net
sink through the bog,
reach down to a forgotten
infancy of granite,
and dredge us
a haul of colours
that play and sparkle
through the smother of bog,
pinks, yellows,
amber and orange.

Your saffron scarf,
filled with wind,
rises over your head

like a halo,
then swings to catch
the back of your neck
like a sickle.

The next instant
the dark returns
this sweep of rotting land,
shrunken and vacant.

Listen,
you can almost hear
the hunger falling
back into itself.

This is no place
to be.

With the sun
withdrawn,
the bog wants to sink,
break
the anchor of rock
that holds it up.

We are left.

There is no one
who knows us.

In our monotone
we beg the bound stone
for our first echo.

Gabriel Rosenstock

10 OF MY FAVOURITE SCOTS-GAELIC TERMS FOR SEAWEED

FEAMAINN

STRAILLEACH

TACHAIR

                RAMASG

                    SGUILLEACH

                        MAOIS

ROP

BRUCHDA-DUBH

RATH

SGRIB-GHEARRAIDH!

John B. Keane

THE MEMORY WRITES

Dear Brain,

I recall a votive mass commissioned by your loving mother for the fulfilment of her private intentions. Your father had gone to his grave but six months earlier and if there are choirs of angels in the regions beyond they were surely gathered in their entirety to sing that sainted soul into heaven.

For his likes, heaven if there is one, with its indescribable effulgence and pain-free felicity, was most certainly devised as a just need for his humanitarian activities during his all too short stay in this crucible we call the world.

You were in your late teens and, like all mothers, yours still cherished delusory hopes that you might yet entertain a vocation for the priesthood. The votive candles shimmered in their polished candelabra and no sound save the rustle of the sacred vestments obtruded into that solemn place other than yours and your mother's gentle breathing.

How is it that occasions like these which are designated to impose pious sentiments on the participants very often induce responses which are far from spiritual, responses alas which are the direct opposite of those intended. I am only your memory and cannot choose what you wish to recall. I am a good memory and I store much that is eminently quotable and well worth visual replay, but you prefer to summon up the less savoury aspects of your tainted past.

Instead of praying for your father's soul you permitted your mind to wander to a visit of Connelly's Circus when it had played a matinee in your childhood,and what was it you thought of? The elephants, the lions, and horses and ponies, the juggler, the monkeys? No indeed, oh most lascivious of wretches! Even in the sacred place where you and your mother came to worship you might have been partially forgiven if you had remembered Loco the red-nosed, potbellied clown who had every child under the canvas in stitches.

Earlier that morning I had high hopes for you. Quite unexpectedly and delightfully you recalled glimpses of the snowy summits of the South Kerry mountains in all their pearly whiteness as they strove to survive the warming winds of a bright May morning. There is a godly gleam from mountain snow when the sun assails it. I would have forgiven you if this recollection had persisted throughout the celebration of the holy mass for there is a deep spirituality secreted in the beauties of nature, a spirituality so glorious that God is forever manifesting Himself and his artistry through its magnificent intricacies.

No such lofty pursuits for you, however, who preferred to resurrect the only scene in that particular circus which provoked criticism from the local parish priest, who described it as obscene. That was when Mona Bonelli, the Italian contortionist, wearing a skintight suit, only the skimpiest of briefs and the barest of bras, danced on to the centre ring under the spotlight's glare. Her dazzling smile captivated all present but you more than any. Immediately she lifted the hoop through which she would thrust her seemingly boneless body you started to drool and slobber like a starving hound on beholding a string of blushing pork sausages. Granted the girl was sensual and sinuous, even voluptuous when she felt so disposed, but there was a hardness and a craftiness about her which you refused to recognise.

All that concerned you was the way she displayed her shapely body as she twisted and screwed her muscular limbs. There were, I will concede, no angles to her, no warps nor wrinkles nor blemish that could be perceived by the naked eye. With curves she was bountifully endowed and aided by the make-up, the perpetual smile, the shimmering sequins on her scant apparel and the bright spotlights she did succeed in unsettling the less discerning and non-artistic males among the audience.

Long before her performance drew to a close you were completely carried away, and to think that you would preserve this far-off exhibition for the sacred occasion devoted to your father's memory.

I have forgotten the number of times you have recalled Mona Bonelli and countless other scantily clad and unclad visions to induce nocturnal slumber when by the simple expedient of saying your night-time prayers your conscience would just as easily have entrusted you to the waiting arms of Morpheus.

You could not know, of course, poor, weak-willed organ, that the glamorous Mona Bonelli was in reality none other than plain Biddy Muldoon from the county of Waterford and that she was not the nineteen year old titian-haired beauty that she was supposed to be. Rather was she a forty-year-old mousey-haired, drop-out housewife who had allowed herself some years before to be seduced and latterly taken in tow by the moustachioed ringmaster of Connelly's Circus. Her deserted husband had ever after made it a point to remember the ringmaster in his prayers, day and night, "For," said he to a freshly acquired helpmate, "he has taken the scourge of my life upon himself and heaven will surely be his lot, for he will suffer his hell in this world."

Later that evening, the same Mona Bonelli or Biddy Muldoon was seated in the local hotel where your father had invited you to partake of an orangeade whilst he sampled the excellent potstill whiskey for which the hostelry was renowned. Mona Bonelli, the luscious, titian-haired teenager from the land of the Tiber and the Po was now showing every single one of her forty years and deprived of the glamorous aids of her contortionist's trade she looked a very ordinary creature indeed. You failed to recognise her and even when she vainly tried to ogle your late, lamented father by crossing and uncrossing her still shapely legs you still could not call to mind the body that had transported you such a short while before.

I can never comprehend why you still persist in remembering the more tawdry experiences of your past, especially since I carry a large stock of beautiful visions which you would have no trouble remembering if only you made the effort. Among other things I have an excellent range of truly beautiful faces including those of your aging mother and your long-suffering spouse and, of course, the innocent faces of your children. I lovingly preserve those of your maiden aunts and benevolent uncles and, dare I mention her name, the lovely Lily Lieloly. No memory could be blamed for cherishing that angelic face.

I have an exciting repertoire of sporting occasions from the lowliest of donkey derbies to the heart-stopping drama of the Aintree Grand National, from your own humble contributions on the playing fields to the dizzy heights of the great Olympics. No television set will ever serve you as well as I do and yet you all too often employ me to recall the basest of your activities.

I have priceless accumulation of sunsets, no two of which are alike, and were you to excavate my recesses you would find such an array of wonders treasured over a lifetime that your heart would be permanently uplifted. There are my vaults of cloud formations, cataracts, dawns, twilights, sunbeams and, of course, my seascapes ever ready to reveal themselves.

Remember the blizzards, the cloudbursts and the fuming, raging anger of the oceans. Remember the rolling reverberations of the great thunderstorms, the crackling, the booming and the lingering echoes as the turmoil spent itself in the all-absorbing bosom of the sky. Remember the surging, sweeping floods, their inestimable passion concealed in the sibilant deceptive surges. Oh those rampant, riotous water, dirging and delving and loamy! I can bring to mind the sound and the pictures in an instant. Just say the word and I will recall for you the first kiss, the first embrace, the first love of those halcyon days when your heart was unsullied and pure. I have so much that is elevating, so much that will bring you closer to the ideal of self-purification, the only ideal which will truly prepare you for the transition from a known state to an unknown. Prompt me, poise me, nudge me to work for your good.

Resist the evil pressures that would have me prostitute my talents so that your unworthy whims might be gratified. Let me resurrect for you the glories and the good deeds, so few in your lifetime to date. Upon recalling these you may go forth and emulate, thus inspiring me to renounce the inglorious and ignominious.

I will conclude now but before I do I would like to recall for you the most heroic incident which might be credited to you. You were but seven then and you were in the company of an even younger girl who happened to be your playmate of the time. As the two of you passed Drumgooley's farmyard gate, having wandered from a rustic picnic organised by your mother, who should come fussing and flapping from the fowl-run but Drumgooley's gander, a fearsome creature with a nerve-shattering cackle whenever he felt his flock was in danger.

Bravely you ordered your young charge to run for her life while you manfully stood your ground and diverted this bloodthirsty barnyard braggart until she had run clear of danger. Allowing for your age and size this was a monumental feat of bravery, of selflessness, of knight-errantry. It was, however, never to be equalled in the long years that followed, but in recalling it I may perhaps remind you that there was a brief but glorious while when chivalry was your long suit.

Finally I would ask you to use me for the betterment of your immortal soul while conceding that I must also be spiced a little now and then if I am to be entertaining as well as exalting.

Sincerely,

Your Memory.

Michael Harding

THE TROUBLE WITH SARAH GULLION:

(Extract)

Everywhere she is cloistered
by the walls of a bungalow or a semidetatched.
Feeling each day prettier than ever.

Waiting.
Always waiting for him to turn the key in the door.
And every night she watches the news,
like a dry weary land without water.

She waits for the leaves to fall
and the bone to wind through the place where the leaves
were.
She waits for the corpse
draped in its flag
holding her cigarette out
to the wind.

Like a black rock she waits
for bones breaking in the night
for boats in a storm;
like a woman in a lounge bar
waiting for her husband.
Waiting to be pregnant.

She is like wallpaper.
The flowered patterns have eased into her marrow.
Her days whirlwind up tunnels of sycamore.

She is sparrow-cocked down corridors
in night journeys;

hospital clocked,
she wanders about
in her pyjamas
looking for the lavatory.

2.

She saw him once at the gable of the street. He came as
close
as the back door. And she knew it was him, for he bared
his
upper teeth when he laughed, and he laughed a lot when
he
saw her squatting on the floor.
And when he was around,
she was frightened at night
by the sounds
in the yard.

3.

He opens the door
of the room where she sleeps.
She untightens her naked body
to accept him.

He reaches his arm out, and blows her head off.
Seven rounds.
To make sure.

Christ have mercy on me, she says,

Lord have mercy
Christ hear me
Christ graciously hear me.
Angel at the window
pray for me
house of the sleepers
pray for me
sticks of light
pray for me
cracks in the silence
pray for me.

All ye who live in the cloister and the woods
pray for me.
All ye who go out in boats
pray for me.

From the dream that withers
O Lord deliver us
From the face in the pool
O Lord deliver us
From the names and addresses
O Lord deliver us
From the warrior who cuts the tree to the root
O Lord deliver us
From the hole in the ditch
and the man in the river
O Lord deliver us

Christ deliver us
Christ hear us
Christ deliver us
Christ graciously hear us.

She said.

She would have said more but she hadn't time.

4.

SCATTER.
That's what they say when a target is hit.
SCATTER.
And the man who did it would fuck off
his hammer still up
and his throat full of pride.
His prayers like a flock of dead birds.

So now the soldier knows everything about her.
Her name,
and her lips.
Her veils and her tents.

And the look in her eyes
as she died.

Michael D Higgins

IN THE BEGINNING

In the beginning was the Word
but the Word was not the beginning.
When the light faded
on the gestures of order
fired at unbroken time
the pieces descended
into darkness
did not arrange themselves
except in arbitrary shape.

Nor was the beginning out of order,
Nor was the word that sought order the beginning.
The Word was an arbitrary shape
beyond gaze and breath.
It was in glorious darkness
out of chaos
the Word came.

That first scream of need
is the beginning
of a long surrender
that is not easily borne.
The struggle for a recovered silence
will never be complete.
And, if the accent is a form of falling,
the look that precedes the word
will stay to haunt.
The breath that interceded
will break forth
in a great screaming grief
of love.

And, if at times the shaking
of the seasonal words
in Gaia's hands
makes rhythms,
it is to remind us
of that time
before the Word.

And, if, in weakness,
we polish the wild words
to make a prayerful set of beads
from the jagged edges of stony times,
or cry out on a Sunday, shadow sated,
then sing our souls
not for the fading of the light
nor yet the ebbing sea.
Through tears,
it is a worn face,
Not white
but ebony,
we see
calling from the darkness
before the Word
and the false promise of order.

The salt of tears
is a deposit in memory
or our sea beginnings.
It is there that is lodged
of all our time
lost in endless space.

Bill Long

A CHANGE OF HEART

The little Oratory in St Vincent's Hospital is indeed an oasis of quiet and peace. The foyer outside the Oratory door is, for at least twelve hours a day, as busy and bustling and noisy as the Arrivals Terminal at Dublin Airport. Here, at the veritable cross-roads of the whole hospital, they have two shops, a busy Accounts Office, an information desk, and admissions office, a bank cash machine, a change-dispensing machine, service elevators, and a large area with seats where very young children, not allowed into the wards, are accommodated. And there is the constant flux of visitors, nurses and doctors. But beyond the heavy, polished oak door of the Oratory, is another world. A small, circular world of individual oak seats and prie-dieus, a carved granite altar, and an absence of the vulgar statuary and fussy fitments that so often debase such places, distracting the mind and inhibiting any meaningful thought, prayer, or meditation. Freshly cut flowers adorn the altar, glowing in the burnished light filtered through the stained glass windows. A tiny lamp burns perpetually before the tabernacle. The soothing odour of flowers, old wood and wax polish permeates. The aura of peace and quiet saturating the place is tangible. All this helped by the fact that it is never crowded. I have never seen more than three or four people there at one time. The occasional visitor; but usually patients, in dressing gowns and slippers like myself, seeking some surcease from the monotony of life in the wards; needing a climate conducive to meditation and prayer. The only sounds I have ever heard here are an occasional, unbidden, heart-felt, heart-rending sigh and a muttered, sottovoce... "Jesus, mercy" or "Mary, help!" I have often wondered sitting here, what fears and despairs and hopes are resumed in the accumulated thoughts and prayers and sighs of those who come here in any one day. People like myself awaiting life-saving surgery; others recovering; others with terminal illnesses. All forced by illness, of one kind or other, to the ultimate confrontation, the moment of truth, the coming face-to-face with God, and consequently with themselves.

Nurse comes for me and I reluctantly leave. As we go I look back at the exhortation above the entrance: "Be still and know that I am God."

It is now almost Easter and I should be well enough to go home for the holiday. I am on some trial medication which is keeping me stabilised and relatively pain free. Just the occasional anginal attack. More than the attack itself I dislike the treatment for it; two quick sprays of nitro-glycerine from the little red aerosol I carry always on my person. The side-effects: nausea and a splitting headache, and the awful aftertaste, lingering like a reminder of death on the palate.

Brendan Kennelly

FUTURE GUILT

The mountain is judging me tonight.
I've been hauled here into the Black Valley
And made to stand before that tribunal.
A few stars have scurried away in terror
And hidden their faces in darkness beyond darkness.
The moon spits, gives a sneering grin
That in a tick disfigures time and space.
What is my sin?

The mountain is listening.
Some new stars are giving evidence,
Their faces made of hate, their tongues filthy.

The jury of planets doesn't miss a thing
And the verdict makes sense.
Guilty. The mountain repeats it. Guilty.
I will be sentenced in the Black Valley.
When I hear it pronounced in appropriate tones
I don't know what to make of the sentence:

I'm to bear the weight of the mountain's shadow
Till my blood vanishes and my bones
Melt. Wherever I travel on earth
The mountain's shadow will be mine.
Day and night in sun and wind and ice and rain
Nothing I do will shake it off.
The more I struggle to be free
The more it will burden and entangle me.
I must never protest or question
Because when the mountain passes sentence

On a man, it's the end, or the beginning, as you will.
The shadow I cast now is mountain-huge, and growing
still.
If follows me like future guilt,
Stretches before me like my past
A malignant judge who'll never rest
Till he's convicted me of waste
And sentenced me to a black hole
In the middle of my heart:
I'll be a lump of writhing dust
Hating the thought of what I am.

Therefore, one evening, late September,
Sauntering down an empty street
I strangle my own shadow.
    I do, I know I do.

Forever and forever I'll remember
My strangled shadow in the mild light.
If shadows die this death is true.
If not, shadows lie too.

Sam McAughtry

TIRED OF LIFE

In the spring of 1929 I decided to run away from home. I was eight years of age. It must have been spring because the grass was damp during running away hours, and the reason I know the grass was damp is that I had resolved to sit on the damp grass on purpose, after running away, get the cold and sicken and die, and teach my mother a thorough-going lesson for what she had done to me. Which was as follows:

I was standing at the door of our house in Cosgrave Street when Davy McAuley and Frankie Pattison walked past.

'Where are you going?' I asked them.

'We're going to Joe's," they said, "are you coming?"

They meant the picture house owned by a man called Joe McKibbin. A pleasure palace where, for a penny, you could occupy twelve inches of wooden form, breathe in concentrated disinfectant, and scream at the antics of Charlie Chaplin, or Buster Keaton, or a hundred other heroes.

But I hadn't any pennies. In the circumstances, Plan X was indicated.

"I'm not going to the pictures," I shouted at the top of my voice. "I've no money, and my mother won't give me a penny."

The plan worked perfectly at the start. Before I had even closed my mouth the kitchen door was flung open, a soapy hand came out, and I was hauled inside the house, coming to rest by the washtub where mother spent most of her waking hours. I tensed myself for the sudsy slap across the back of the leg. Sure enough it arrived. Then Plan X allowed for a tongue-lashing for showing mother up in front of the neighbours, and this, too, arrived on schedule. The last part of the calculation foresaw a penny being crammed into my hand and myself being hurled back outside again, to set off with my mates to the pictures.

Not so. All I got was hurled outside. No penny. No nothing. I made up my mind to run away.

Up Cosgrave Street, up the Limestone Road, and into

Alexandra Park. There I sat deliberately on the damp grass in order to kill myself.

After about three minutes I was beginning to think it wasn't the greatest way to go. I rose, pulled my trousers away from the skin, and decided instead to climb up and touch the screen the next time I went to the pictures. Everybody knew the screen was full of electricity. I could shout at the horrified audience: "This is my mother's fault," and then touch the screen.

I was interrupted in my planning by a voice, calling me: "D'ye want to see a bird's nest?"

It was a boy from the Limestone Road district. He beckoned me over to a hawthorn bush. Sure enough there was a nest, round and snug. But it was empty.

"Don't touch it," the boy warned me, "or they won't come back to it. They can smell if you touch it."

We stared at it for a bit and then wandered down to the almost deserted swings, occupying one each.

"What school do you go to?" the other asked.

"Barney's," I told him, giving him the nickname of St. Barnabas'".

"I go to the Star of the Sea," he said.

I looked at him with interest. "What's it like?" I wanted to know.

"Rotten," he replied, "you get hit with the tawse for nothing."

"We get hit with the cane for nothing," I said. "Last week I got six slaps just for climbing up a spout. Barney's is stinking," I told him, with feeling. But there was something I wanted this fellow to clear up. "Tell me this," I asked him, "do you have to drink holy water in the Star of the Sea?"

My companion turned round on his swing and looked at me as if I was ready to be certified. "You don't drink holy water," he said patiently, "are you stupid or something?"

Before I could pursue the matter any further the other boy jumped off his swing and, giving himself a two-length start, challenged me to a race over to the river.

The river was actually a narrow stream. It was full of minnows. Off came our slippers to be shoved in our pockets, and we began to co-operate in the catching of minnows. Working as a skilled team we surrounded and scooped up a good dozen minnows, letting them off again because we had no jampot to keep them in. As the afternoon wore on we gradually worked our way upstream until we had reached the point where it emerged in Alexandra Park after its journey under the Antrim Road from the Corporation Waterworks. When we were too cold to stand it any longer we rubbed each other's toes with grass to warm them up, then we put our canvas slippers back on again.

"I go home this way," the boy from the Limestone Road said, pointing to a hole in the boundary hedge where thousands of boys before him had punched an entrance to the Antrim Road. He turned back to me before he left: "Will you be here tomorrow?" he asked.

"I don't know," I told him, "I might kill myself. But if I don't," I finished, "I'll see you beside the bird's nest after school."

Then I went on my way home. The family were all sitting up to the tea when I walked in. Without interrupting their eating they moved up to make room for me.

I couldn't help thinking whenever I sat down at the table that not one of them had even noticed that I had run away and returned again. I decided to run away properly the next day. Either that or deliberately choke myself to death with bread and butter.

Conor O'Callaghan

THE BALCONY

after Montale

It seemed like a simple game
to change to nothing the space
before me, and to indefinite
tedium your more definite flame.

Now at that void I have gathered
each of my latent motives.
Over sheer blankness stirs
the need to wait on you alive.

A glimmering world is
the only one you can see.
You lean out towards it
from this window that is unlit.

Gioia Timpanelli

THE REGULAR LIFE OF WILD THINGS
(for G.S., May 8, 1989)

They used to come regularly at 10:30 and 4:00: wild turkeys walking silently, single file in and out of white birch. My husband counted 22 from the upstairs window, watching until they were out of sight. That was early October. A way into December we asked each other, "Have you seen the turkeys today?" The answer was always, "No." All December there was no sign of them. Then, on the last day of the month, I heard a throaty cry at dusk deep in the pines. Ah, they are still around, I thought, comforted.

In January wild turkeys were *not* around. Neither of us on our walks heard or saw signs of them: no dog delight in droppings, no turkey stir-abouts under the old oaks, no red fox walking briskly or stopping to smell the air. Then once in the middle of a conversation with visitors and apropos of nothing, I said,"Perhaps the turkeys are passing." We went laughing to the window but they weren't there. From that time on we talked about them to everyone who came to the house: friends, relatives, a lineman, a parcel delivery woman, and to even a lost hiker. "Have you ever seen the wild turkeys who live here?" The answer was always, "No," some with interest, some with none. "They're big" we said, "four feet high; that's big for a bird," we said. (And they have brilliant bronze and green feathers, those colors so varied they're difficult to describe. Once I saw a male fan his tailfeathers, showing two unexpected contrasting striped chevrons—the kind of beauty you see in an old Japanese print.) But all the talk yielded us nothing. No sight of turkeys all January. "Perhaps they've all been killed in hunting season," suggested more than one guest. No, we felt, no; they've done this before, haven't they? But we couldn't remember.

The first week of February was warm and then suddenly cold. Yesterday on a walk in the woods I found an old logging trail and there crossing the road were three fresh sets of turkey tracks deep in the frozen snow. Their size was startling. All of a sudden, I knew the tracks had shown an old and yet apparent secret about tricky time. And we had had pterodactyls living near us all the while.

I have been playing all morning with an excitement, knowing that soon we will see them again. Now we can say we missed them, had begun to think their presence essential; we had marked their comings and goings lightly but it was here in our chests that we had missed them, missed a particular bearing, an unexpected movement, a specific beauty, their pattern of ordinary necessity.

Pat Ingoldsby

IT ISN'T

She said
"I was waiting
at a bus stop
when a rhinoceros
came rampaging
along the Clontarf Road
and I wasn't wearing
my glasses
so I thrust out my hand
to stop it
but it thundered on past.
"Did you see that?"
I said to the very
short squat man
beside me.
"The bus didn't stop."
"You'll have to excuse me"
he said. "I'm not wearing
my glasses but as far
as I could see
you were attempting
to hail a haystack
with legs."
Then she put on her glasses
and discovered that
she had been conversing
with a litter bin.
He put on his glasses
and discovered that
she wasn't there
at all.

Helen Vendler

THE TEACHER, THE STUDENT, AND LITERATURE

Those of us who teach literature were once, of course, students of literature; and the student of literature has always, to begin with, been a reader of literature. The writers of literature were all readers to begin with, too; and most of them became students of literature; some of them became, and still become, teachers of literature. In short, the chain is one of densely-intertwined links: readers, students, writers, and teachers are the same person, we might say, at different stages. Whether or not the reader, the student, and the teacher become writers is often a matter of chance; the remarkable record, in America, of the Federal Writer's Project in the depression in making writers out of blacks who might otherwise not have found their vocation (Ralph Ellison, Richard Wright, and Arna Bontemps all worked for the Project) suggests that social discouragement can open possibilities to potential writers just as social encouragement can close them. In Iceland, I have been told, it is considered a civic duty to write a book; before you die, you should leave a record, in some way, of what it meant to live in Iceland in your era and in your community: the saga-tradition should not be interrupted.

Teaching, too, is a form of writing—not with ink, with speech— after the manner of composition of the story-tellers, saga-reciters, and oral commentators or homilists. It is a form of embroidery around the thing itself. When the embroidery is written down, we call it criticism or reviewing or annotation or commentary. But it is all part of the same process—by which the rabbis of the Talmud embroidered the Torah, or the monks of the monasteries glossed the Gospels, or the directors of Shakespeare reimagined the plays. Inside every great text lies the potential to generate new versions of itself. Most of these versions are generated in the classroom, where thousands of teachers, over hundreds of generations, have perpetuated the texts by creating, together with their students, communal versions of the classic texts.

It is an odd fact that not even the most gifted readers become readers all by themselves. Reading is an act that requires a mentor— somebody older, who has sifted out the texts for the student, who can pass on the oral tradition of commentary (what is there to be said about a text? why do we want to say things about texts?) and who can, at times, perform the indispensable service of reading well aloud, ensuring the persistence of the oral origins of literature. Some writers have wondered why it is not enough for the student simply to read books, and find mentors on the written page of criticism: Newman, answering that objection in *The Idea of a University,* wrote that it was "the living face, the breathing voice, the expressive countenance", that first, and best meditated knowledge to the young.

And it is the most gifted readers, paradoxically, who need a mentor most, one who reveals to them in the widest way what their own natures are fitted for. The single most heartfelt letter to a teacher ever written was Keat's verse-letter to his high-school teacher Charles Cowden Clarke: Clarke not only taught Keats, he loaned him books and talked to him about them. "You first taught me", Keats wrote in return, "all the sweets of song":

> Who read for me the sonnet swelling loudly
> Up to its climax and then dying proudly?
> Who found for me the grandeur of the ode,
> Growing, like Atlas, stronger from its load?...
> Shew'd me that epic was of all the king,
> Round, vast, and spanning all like Saturn's ring?

We can only can only imagine, with our less eager natures, what it must have meant to Keats when he first heard a sonnet, or saw the burden of the ode growing to a rich power, or felt the planetary reach of an epic. But Keats was writing this poem at 21, and he had first encountered Clarke before he was 14: it is for that reason that Keats next takes on the theme of the benefits, in subsequent years, of his hours with Clarke:

> Ah! had I never seen,
> Or known your kindness, what might I have been?
> What my enjoyments in my youthful years,
> Bereft of all that now my life endears?
> And can I e'er these benefits forget?
> And can I e'er repay the friendly debt?
> No, doubly no.

This early (and still inept) poem retains as its chief charm the sketch of an ideal relation between literature, the teacher, and the student. Literature is presented in the form of an immemorial canon of genres—the sonnet, the ode, the epic; the teacher is presented as reading, as talking, and as guiding; and the student is presented in two phases of his life—in the classroom and in a subsequent life endeared by poetry, indebted to the benefits conferred by the teacher. It is not the only possible sketch of a valuable relation, but it sets us a standard that we all recognise, and that we all aim at.

But we fail at it, too. And because we can fail, and do, I think it is worth considering how we succeed, and why; and how we fail, and why. All of us have good and bad tales to tell about ourselves, whether as students, as teachers, or as writers. It is characteristic, to come to the first thing that the verse-letter tells us, that Keats writes this letter to the man who taught him poetry. We have no verses from Keats to the men who taught him Latin or mathematics or history, though they may have been as worthy in their way as Charles Cowden Clarke. We all teach best the students who will love what we love; we were ourselves good students for the teachers who led us to paths we find congenial. Nobody can be the ideal teacher for everybody; nobody can be the ideal student for every teacher. Some of our failures can be ascribed to a simple mismatching. The conjunction of teacher and student is a mysterious one with many parallels in the history of love and friendship; it is unequal, but less so than the relation between parent and child; when it succeeds it joins minds, temperaments, and hearts in a subject which is a mutual passion. It fails when these faculties in two people do not align themselves in congruence. If a common passion is the first link between teacher and student, Keats' poem also tells us that the second link is the elaboration of that passion which we call learning. The teacher offers the tradition of interpretation by reading aloud; he explains distinctions of genre; he describes the formal structures of poetry; and he presents a hierarchy of value. In short (Keats implies) the teacher knows as well as loves the subject; and pursues it without distraction or digression. From him, as model, the student learns not only the subject but the attitudes of learning itself. When a teacher is indifferent, students sense that dissatisfaction all too quickly, especially if they have a jealousy for the honour of the text. The teacher, too, judges the seriousness of the students just as they judge him; he respects in the student that alertness of glance that shows a mind that is following the text, the accuracy in words that shows a sense of the author's intent, the thorough absorption of texts that shows on a well-written paper. And finally, students find in each other, ideally, that common conversation that hates to end, that prolongs the class in after-hours talk, that creates friendships that sometimes last from school days to death. Keats says of himself and Clarke:

> [We] revel'd in a chat that ceased not
> When at night-fall among your books we got:
> No, not when supper came, nor after that,—
> Nor when reluctantly I took my hat;
> No, nor till cordially you shook my hand
> Mid-way between our homes.

The chief requisite for the ideal connection of author, teacher, and student is that reality be touched upon. The claim of literature upon us is that it reveals reality. It does this not by any common documentary aim, though that is part of its appeal, but rather by forming a burning glass, or focus, or vanishing point of perspective, around which other forms of reality fall into intelligibility. In this way, the tangled web of random circumstance can be unravelled, and reality be given a purpose and clarification hitherto unknown. The great dead teachers, although they are alive only in books, remain teachers in this way, as Duns Scotus of Oxford remained, some 600 years after his death, a teacher for Hopkins:

Yet ah! this air I gather and release
He lived on; these weeds, these waters, these walls are what
He haunted who of all men most sways my spirits to peace;
Of reality the rarest-veined unraveller, a not
Rivalled spirit.

Hopkins uses the present tense for Duns Scotus' effect on him: he, of all men, says Hopkins, "most sways my spirits to peace" by unravelled reality. Living teachers, too, have unravelled reality for perplexed students by conveying how the interpreting mind of the author objectifies inner experience, and thereby makes it knowable.

But students need various methods, and follow different paths, to come to the recognition that literature is about their own reality. All of us recall a stunning moment in our own past when we first saw that literature was about us, as well as about Hamlet. The moment of autobiographical recognition makes all intense subsequent reading possible; and we should be willing, as teachers, to try any strategy that will lead our students to that moment (as, on the other hand, we must try any strategy that will make them recognise the non-naturalistic stylisation inherent in any art-work). For many students, the moment of autobiographical recognition can only come from studying literature in a thematic way—by our giving them the literature of love, or women's studies, or ethnic studies, or the literature of their own nation or region. The student can then make that crucial identification of his own voice with the author's voice, of his own interests with the author's interests, from which the initial entry into literature is made. In such a moment, by such methods, we can bring together in a shared inner life the teacher, the one taught, and the author. If our students find in such thematic groupings a way to the authentic connection, then such courses are justified, from them we can send students fortified by the experience of the connection with an author out to a wider experience with writers linked to them perhaps not by ethnicity or gender or nationality but by other eventually powerful links of temperament or common interest.

A final indispensable requisite for the connection between the teacher, the student, and literature is that literary writing continue to be done. In a culture where this sort of writing lapses, the teaching of texts lapses too: we see this phenomenon in cultures where free writing is banned, and where literature disappears with it from the schools, as it did for years in China. Students sense, even if obscurely, the dependence of schooling in literature on the continued writing of literature in their own time; and the obdurate tenacity of the writer against all conceivable obstacles to writing comes through to us, when we are students, as we read of Shakespeare's obscure origins, of Pope's "long disease, [his] life", of Keats' poverty, of Tennyson's struggles in his unmanageable family, of Whitman's lack of education, of Stevens' composing after a day of office-work. Nothing guarantees the seriousness of writing like its persistence against obstruction into old age, sickness, and death. The writers and teachers who convey that persistence to us make us think the effort worth a lifetime's devotion. Robert Lowell and Wallace Stevens both wrote about Santayana in this vein: though Santayana had been a famous teacher, philosopher, and poet, he had been largely forgotten by the time of his last illness, when he was nearly ninety. And yet from his hospital bed in Rome, he continued, though he was nearly blind, to correct galley proofs of his last book and send them off to the printer. Lowell saw him, in this scholarly persistence, as an emblem of the teacher and writer as hero in the arena of the mind. Santayana has to use a red crayon to make his galley corrections, and has to use a magnifying glass to see the print. He is, Lowell thinks, a secular Christian martyr whose faith moves the devouring lions of the Colosseum to meekness:

> Old trooper, I see your child's red crayon pass,
> bleeding deletions on the galleys you hold
> under your throbbing magnifying glass,
> that worn arena, where the whirling sand
> and broken-hearted lions lick your hand
> refined by bile as yellow as a lump of gold.

> (For George Santayana)

When Stevens was taught by Santayana, he brought Santayana a sonnet he had written: Santayana wrote a sonnet in return that very day. This almost Japanese courtesy and reciprocity between teacher and student is scarcely possible in the larger university milieu of these days; but the model of Santayana reading proof depends on no reciprocity, only on a single-minded absorption by the teacher in the truth of his own utterance. If, as students, we have seen such a teacher—even as spectators in a large lecture class where we were not ourselves known—we have been shown what exactness and patience in knowledge can be. If, on the other hand, we see a teacher—or, as teachers, see ourselves—playing to the gallery, and choosing performance over fidelity to truth, we are ashamed, because the better model persists within us as a reproach.

It is clear to us all that we have been lucky if we have found one or two teachers in our lifetime that were the best teachers for us— teaching us a subject we found congenial with a mind we could respect, unravelling reality for us through the text, and absorbed in the work of utterance, whether in speech or in writing. More often than not, at least one of the ideal conditions is lacking, and we find uncongenial teachers for congenial subjects, or a text in which we or the teacher cannot find the vein of reality, or a slant of mind in the teacher that rubs us the wrong way, or a theatricality in the teacher that we distrust. Sometimes (to turn to ourselves as teachers) we have been assigned uncongenial topics, or thrown together with the wrong group of students, or asked to teach a small class when we are better at large ones, or vice versa. Inexperience, shyness, and social awkwardness stand between teachers and students; the barriers of historical time and alien language stand between students and texts. The whole frail bridge of literary teaching and learning is so ill-constructed and threatened by odd loadings that it is a wonder that it holds at all—still more of a wonder that it becomes, at its best, a Jacob's ladder with angels passing up and down on it, linking our earth with the heaven of the poets, that "artifice of eternity".

Reading, studying, teaching, and writing are strange, immensely complex, and unquantifiable activities. They are, however, unwieldy as they are, the only method the race has found for conveying down through the ages tat inner life of feeling and thinking and language which is all that distinguishes us from the animals. It is no wonder that we teach badly; the wonder is that we do it at all. In spite of the breakdowns of the system, which are real and discouraging for us all, we continue, as students and teachers, to be like Whitman's noiseless patient spider, launching forth filament, filament, filament, in measureless oceans of space.

> Ceaselessly musing, venturing, throwing, seeking the spheres to connect them,
> Till the bridge you will need be form'd. till the ductile anchor hold,
> Till the gossamer thread you fling catch somewhere, O my soul,

As students, we have all been caught at least once by that gossamer thread; as teachers, we hope to form the bridge again.

Michael Longley

BETWEEN HOVERS

in memory of Joe O'Toole

And not even when we ran over the badger
Did he tell me he had cancer, Joe O'Toole
Who was psychic about carburettor and clutch
And knew a folk cure for the starter-engine.
Backing into the dark we floodlit each hair
Like a filament of light our lights had put out
Somewhere between Kinnadoohy and Thallabaun.
I dragged it by two gritty paws into the ditch.
Joe spotted a ruby where the canines touched.
His way of seeing me safely across the duach
Was to leave his porch light burning, its sparkle
Shifting from widgeon to teal on Corragaun Lake.
I missed his funeral. Close to the stony roads
He lies in Killeen Churchyard over the hill.
This morning on the burial mound at Templedoomore
Encircled by a spring tide and taking in
Cloonaghmanagh and Claggan and Carrigskeewaun,
The townlands he'd wandered tending cows and sheep,
I watched a dying otter gaze right through me
At the islands in Clew Bay, as though it were only
Between hovers and not too far from the holt.

Tommy Sands and Pete Seeger

THE MUSIC OF HEALING

The cease fires in Northern Ireland brought a great sense of hope to us all. No matter what the eventual solution is to be, ordinary people will have to gather up the pieces and learn to live together. Sometimes Music can help to heal some of the wounds. I wrote this song with the help of a great hero of mine who has become a great friend, Pete Seeger.

I'm delighted that Pete and his grandson Tao were able to join me on this recording. Thanks to Greg and Lisa for setting up the session in New York and to Vedran Smailovic for joining us on cello. Every day in his native Sarajevo, the lone figure of Smailovic, dressed in full evening suit could be seen, walking past his bombed out orchestra theatre and in the street, amidst shell and fire he sat down and played is cello for peace. When a CNN reporter asked him if he was not crazy for playing his cello in the middle of the shelling the famous Smailovic reply that went all around the world was, "You ask me am I crazy...why do you not ask those people on the mountain are they not crazy for shelling Sarajevo while Smailovic is playing the cello?".

Don't beat the drum, that frightens the children
Don't sing the songs about winning and losing
Sit down beside me, the green fields are bleeding
Sing me the music of healing
Sing me a song of a lover returning
The darker the night, the nearer the morning
Bring me the news of a new day that's dawning
Sing me the music of healing

Chorus

Ah, the heart's a wonder
Stronger than the guns of thunder
Even when we're torn asunder
Love will come again

Sometimes the truth's like a hare in the cornfield
You know that it' there but you can't put your arms round
it
All we can hope for is follow its footprints
Sing me the music of healing
Who would have thought I could feel so contented
To learn I was wrong after all of my rambles
I've learned to be hard and I've learned how to tremble
Sing me the music of healing

Somehow the cycle of vengeance keeps turning
Till each other's sorrows and songs we start learning
Peace is the prize for this who are daring
Sing me the music of healing
Time is your friend, it cures all your sorrows
But how can I wait for another tomorrow
One step today and a thousand will follow
Sing me the music of healing

Gordon Snell

MRS BEETON

The guests who dined with Mrs Beeton
Were sure to find they'd overeaten.
Whole herds of cows and shoals of fishes
Were used to make her famous dishes.

She had a bucket as a scoop
To ladle out the oxtail soup.
The whipped cream piled upon her trifle
Rose higher than the Tower of Eiffel.

In every dish, her books inform us,
The quantities must be enormous;
For Mrs Beeton took the view:
Why use one egg, when twelve will do?

How those Victorian gents indulged!
No wonder that their waistcoats bulged.
They gorged on goose, munched mounds of
        mutton,
And then undid another button.

Oh, lucky gents! They'd think us bats
To fear cholesterol and fats.
They exercised, when they were able,
By simply lurching from the table.

Now, in this era of the Slimmer,
Poor Mrs. Beeton's fame grows dimmer.
Though many still enjoy her diet,
They have to do it, on the quiet.

Michael Hartnett

A PRAYER FOR SLEEP
For Geraldine W.

Grant me good rest tonight oh Lord:
let no creatures prowl
the tangled pathways in my skull;
wipe out all wars,
throw Guilt a bone;
let me dream (if I dream at all)
no child of Yours has come to harm.

I know, of course, that Death's the norm,
that there are people who have yet to climb
all the Present's rungs, who lag behind—
hyaenas at the rim of civilisation's light—
whose laughing hides a Stone-Age howl,
who wait 'til lights go down to pounce
and rip the guts of Progress out.

Yet grant me good rest tonight my Lord,
blind my internal eyes;
guard my fifty baffled years
with Your protecting arm
and let me dream (if I dream at all)
no child of Yours has come to harm.

A Note From the Editor and Compilers

This Anthology was a project of the Transition Year Class 1994-95 and we are very grateful to the following:-

Deirdre Shannahan, Irene Conneely, Mia McCarthy, Angela Gordon, Tracey Mullen, Brian Cosgrove, Adrian Mitchell, Ronan O'Sullivan, Eamon Guy, Jonathan Faherty, Peter Jefferies, Chris O'Connor, Daniel King, Shane Flaherty, Thomas Early, Elton Heffernan, Alan Gormley, Jason Duanne, John King, David Ward and course co-ordinator Anne Garvey.

And a very special word of thanks to Theo Dorgan whose idea it was to compile the anthology in the first place. To Niamh McGarry for type-setting, and to Niamh Morris for her help.

Emma Conneely also deserves our thanks, and Anne King, John Moriarty and Tomás Hardiman.

For permission to reprint copyright material we are grateful to all the authors and the following:

Glendale Press for Jack Harte's story from *Murphy In The Underworld*, 1986.

The Harvill Press for 'The Hay-Carrier' from *A Snail In My Prime* by Paul Durcan, 1993.

The Dedalus Press for 'Duvet' from *Out of Silence* by Pádraig J. Daly, 1993.

Faber & Faber for 'Saint Kevin and the Blackbird' by Seamus Heaney—collection to be published in 1996.

Also to Faber & Faber for 'Walking On Sunday' from *New Selected Poems* by Richard Murphy.

The Gallery Press for 'Two Gathering', from *So It Goes* by Eamon Grennan, 1995, also for 'The Water Table' from *Sunday School* by Gerald Dawe. Also Gallery Press for 'One Sunday in the Gearagh' from *Time And The Island* and for 'Herbert Park Revisited' from *The Collected Poems,* by John Montague, 1995.

Beaver Row Press for 'Rossadillisk Aubade' from *Return And No Blame*, by Paula Meehan, 1984.

Salmon Poetry - Poolbeg Enterprises for 'Lady Chatterley' by Phil McCarthy, 1994.

For 'Still' by Anne Le Marquand Hartigan from *Immortal Sins*, 1993.

Editor of Irish Times for 'Circle Of Fear' by Nuala O'Faoláin, 30th May, 1995 and 'The Lost Language of Swans' by Michael Viney, 16th November 1994.

Bantam Books for Extract from *Malina* by Penny Perrick, 1993.

Salmon Poetry for 'Anointed' from *Rough Tidings* by Ted McNulty, Galway, 1992, and also for 'Sisyphus' from *The Troubled House*, by Sheila O'Hagan, 1995.

Lilliput Press for *Patera* by Desmond Hogan also excerpt from 'Walking Out To The Islands' from *Setting Foot On The Slopes Of Connemara* by Tim Robinson, 1984.

Brandon Books for 'The Memory Writes' from *Letter To The Brain*, by John B. Keane 1993.

Blackstaff Press for Extract from *The Trouble With Sarah Gullion* by Michael Harding, Belfast 1988.

New Ireland Books for Extract from *A Change Of Heart* by Bill Long, Dublin 1995.

Poolbeg Press for 'Conamara In Our Mind' from *Echoes Of Memory*, by John O'Donohue, Dublin 1994.

Mhia Productions for 'The Search' from *Deccey Lucey Sorts It Out*.

Salmon Publishers for 'The People Who I Grew Up With Were Afraid' by Michael Gorman from *Up She Flew*, 1991.

'Future Guilt' is reprinted by permission of Bloodaxe Books Ltd. from *The Book Of Judas,* by Brendan Kennelly (Bloodaxe Books, 1991) also 'Tight-Wire' from *A Fragile City* by Micheal O'Siadhail.

Blackstaff Press for 'The Gift' from *American Wake* by Greg Delanty.

Thanks to Joe Boske for permission to use poster for cover, Clifden 1992 and also John Foley.

Every effort has been made to get copyright holders' permission. We apologise for any errors or omissions in the above list. We regret that financial constraints and pressure of time meant that we could not include everyone who has read at Clifden Arts Week, but we look forward to incorporating them in our next edition.